101 FOLK SONGS FOR BUSKERS

Piano/Organ Edition with Guitar Chords

Wise Publications
London/New York/Sydney

Exclusive distributors:
Music Sales Limited
8/9 Frith Street,
London W1V 5TZ,
England.

Music Sales Pty Limited
120 Rothschild Avenue,
Rosebery, NSW 2018,
Australia.

This book © Copyright 1989 by
Wise Publications
UK ISBN 0.7119.1357.9
Order No. AM69220

Designed by Helen Senior
Cover illustration by Graham Thompson
Compiled by Peter Evans & Peter Lavender
Music processed by MSS Studios & Hillmob Music Services
Typeset by Capital Setters

Music Sales' complete catalogue lists thousands of titles
and is free from your local music shop,
or direct from Music Sales Limited.
Please send a cheque or Postal order for £1.50 for postage to
Music Sales Limited, 8/9 Frith Street, London W1V 5TZ.

Printed in Great Britain by The Bath Press, Bath

1
AFTON WATER
Traditional

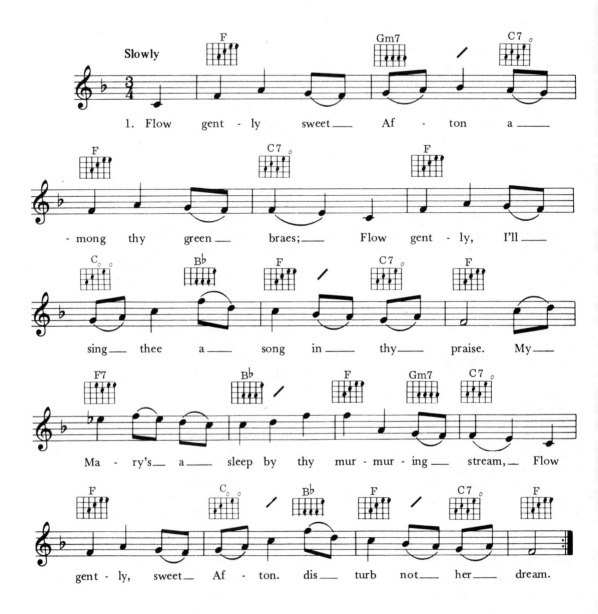

2. Thou stock dove whose echo resounds thro' the glen,
Ye wild whistling blackbirds in yon thorny den,
Thou green crested lap wing, thy screaming forbear,
I charge you disturb not my slumbering fair.

3. Thy crystal stream Afton, how lovely it glides
And winds by the cot where my Mary resides!
How wanton thy waters her snowy feet lave
As, gath'ring sweet flow'rets she stems thy clear wave.

4. Flow gently, sweet Afton among thy green braes,
Flow gently, sweet river, the theme of my lays:
My Mary's asleep by thy murmuring stream,
Flow gently, sweet Afton, disturb not her dream.

A HORSE WITH NO NAME
Words & Music by Dewey Bunnell

Moderately
VERSE

1. On the first part of the jour - ney I was
nine days I let the horse run free 'cause the

look - ing at all the life, There were plants and birds and rocks
des - ert had turned to sea, There were plants and birds and rocks

and things, there were sand and hills and rings. The
and things there were sand and hills and rings. The

first thing I met was a fly with a buzz and the
o - cean is a des - ert with it's life un - der - ground and the

sky with no clouds, The heat was hot and the
per - fect dis - guise a - bove. Un-der the cit - ies lies a

ground was dry, but the air was full of sound. I've
heart made of ground but the hu - mans will give no love. You see I've

3
AMAZING GRACE
Traditional

4
A-ROVING
Traditional

Moderato

1. In Am-ster-dam—there liv'd a maid, mark well what I do say. In
2. I put my arm— a-round her waist, mark well what I do say. I

Am-ster-dam there liv'd a maid and she was mis-tress of her trade. I'll
put my arm a round her waist, says she, "Young man, you're in great haste." I'll

go no more a-rov-ing with you, fair maid.
go no more a-rov-ing with you, fair maid.

Chorus

A-rov-ing, a-rov-ing, Since rov-ing's been my ru-in, I'll

go no more a-rov-ing with you, fair maid.   maid.

3. I took that girl upon my knee,
   Mark well what I do say.
   I took that girl upon my knee,
   Says she, "Young man, you're rather free!"
   I'll go no more a-roving with you fair maids. *(Chorus)*

5
AN ERISKAY LOVE LILT
Words & Music by Kenneth MacLeod &
Marjory Kennedy-Fraser

o_____ ro bhan i Bheir mi o ru o ho 'Smi tha
o_____ ro van ee Vair me o ru o ho Sad am

bròn - ach's tu'm dhith._____ 'Na mo
I with-out thee._____ Thou'rt the
Gur tu

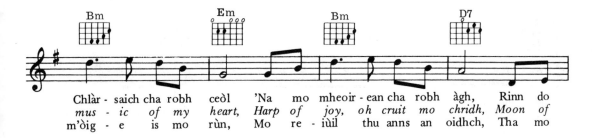

Chlàr - saich cha robh ceòl 'Na mo mheoir - ean cha robh àgh, Rinn do
mus - ic of my heart, Harp of joy, oh cruit mo chridh, Moon of
m'òig - e is mo rùn, Mo re - iùil thu anns an oidhch, Tha mo

phòg - sa mo leon, Fhuair mi Eol - as an dàin. Bheir mi o_____ ro bhan
guid - ance by night, Strength and light thou'rt to me. Vair me o_____ ro van
dhrùidh-eachd ad shùil, Tha mo chiurr - adh ad loinn.

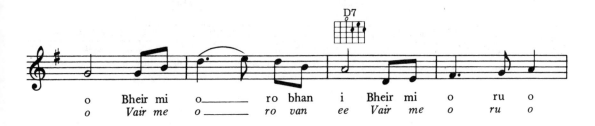

o Bheir mi o_____ ro bhan i Bheir mi o ru o
o Vair me o_____ ro van ee Vair me o ru o

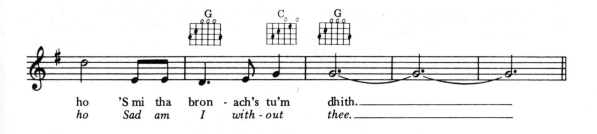

ho 'S mi tha bron - ach's tu'm dhith._____
ho Sad am I with - out thee._____

ARMS OF MARY
Words & Music by Iain Sutherland

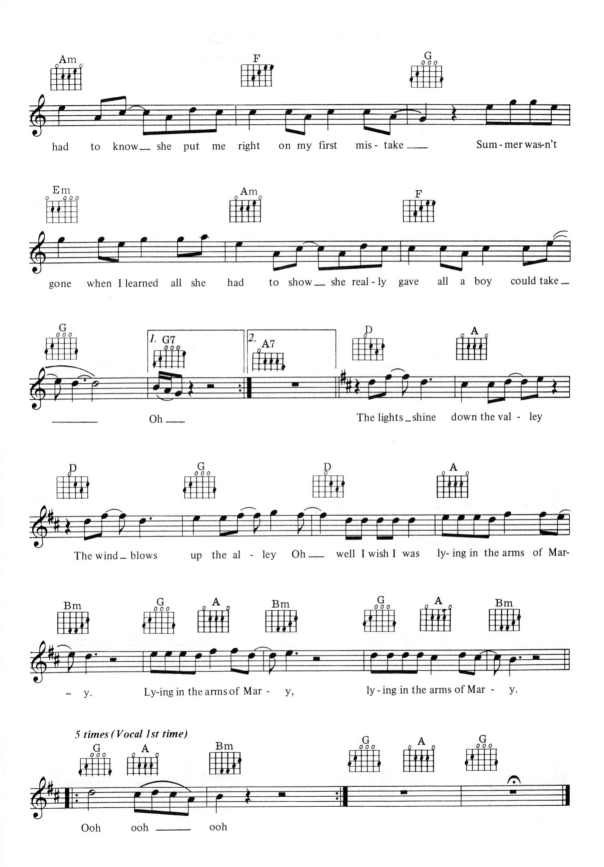

AT SEVENTEEN
Words & Music by Janis Ian

I learned the truth at sev - en - teen_ that love was meant for beau-
brown-eyed girl in hand - me downs_ whose name I nev - er could_

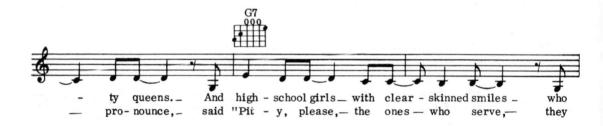

- ty queens._ And high - school girls_ with clear - skinned smiles _ who
— pro - nounce,_ said "Pit - y, please, the ones — who serve,— they

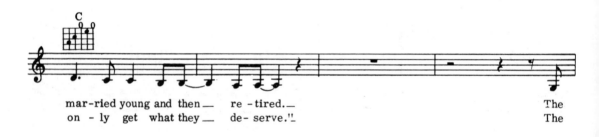

mar-ried young and then _ re -tired._   The
on - ly get what they _ de - serve."_   The

val - en -tines I nev - er knew,_ the Fri - day night cha-rades
rich re - la - tioned home - town queen _ Mar - ries in - to what _

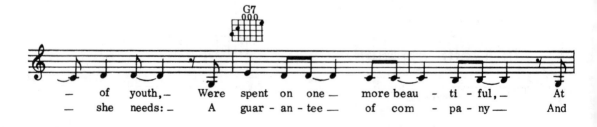

— of youth,_ Were spent on one _ more beau - ti - ful,_ At
— she needs:_ A guar - an - tee _ of com - pa - ny _ And

BANKS OF THE OHIO
Traditional

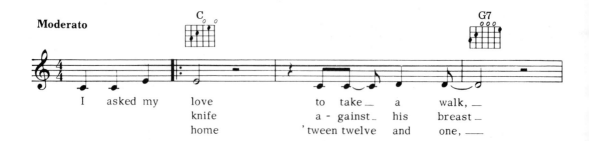

I asked my love to take a walk, —
knife a-gainst his breast —
home 'tween twelve and one, —

To take a walk, — just a lit-tle walk, —
as in-to — my arms he pressed —
I cried,"My God, — what have I done! —

Down be-side _____ where the wat-ers flow, —
He cried,"My love, _____ don't you mur-der me, —
I've killed the on ly man I love." —

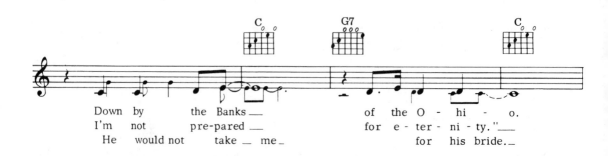

Down by the Banks — of the O-hi - o.
I'm not pre-pared — for e-ter-ni-ty." —
He would not take — me — for his bride. —

And on-ly say   that you'll be mine, _   In no

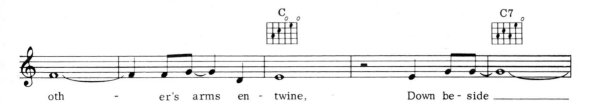

oth   -   er's arms en - twine,   Down be - side _____

where the wa-ters flow _   Down by   the Banks _

[Where the wa-ters   flow   ]

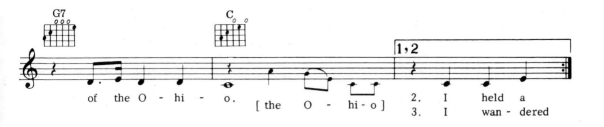

of   the O - hi - o.   2.   I   held   a

[the   O - hi-o]   3.   I   wan - dered

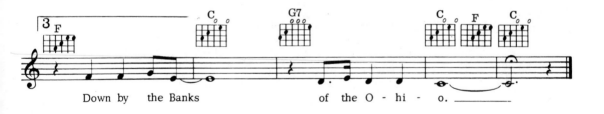

Down by   the Banks   of   the O - hi -   o. _____

BELIEVE ME IF ALL THOSE ENDEARING YOUNG CHARMS

Traditional

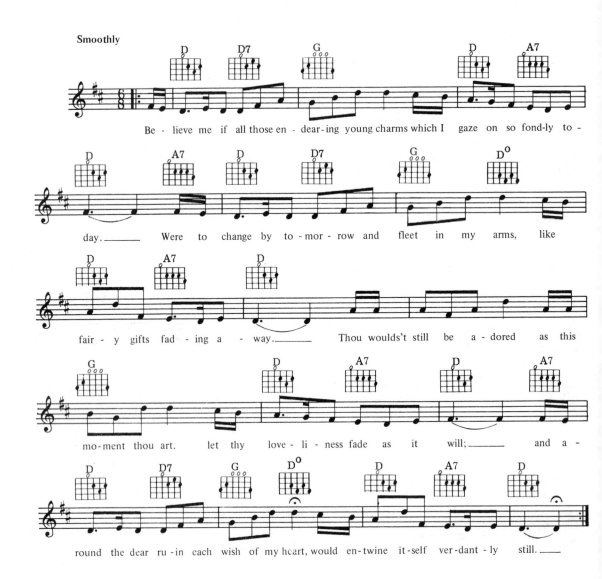

2. It is not while beauty and youth are thine own,
   And thy cheeks unprofan'd by a tear;
   That the fervour and faith of a soul can be known,
   To which time will but make thee more dear!
   No, the heart that has truly lov'd never forgets,
   But as truly loves on to the close;
   As the sunflower turns on her god when he sets
   The same look which she turn'd when he rose.

THE BELLS OF RHYMNEY
Words by Idris Davies
Music by Pete Seeger

(Instrumental) They will
plun - der wil - ly - nil - ly, Cry the bells of Ca - er - phil - ly.
They have fangs they have teeth, Shout the loud bells of
Neath. E - ven God is un - eas - y, Say the
moist bells of Swan - sea. And what will you give me?
Say the sad bells of Rhym - ney. (Instrumental)
Put the van - dals in court,

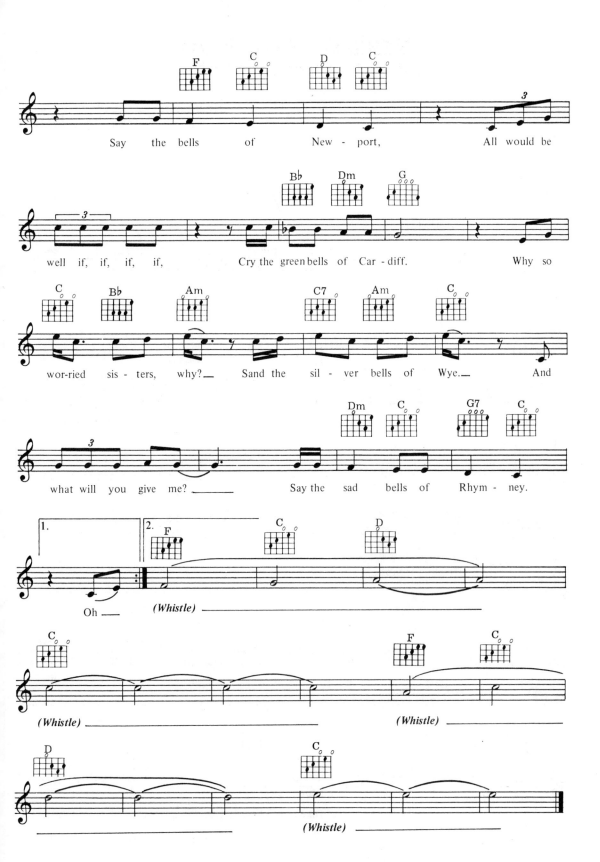

BIRD ON THE WIRE

Words & Music by Leonard Cohen

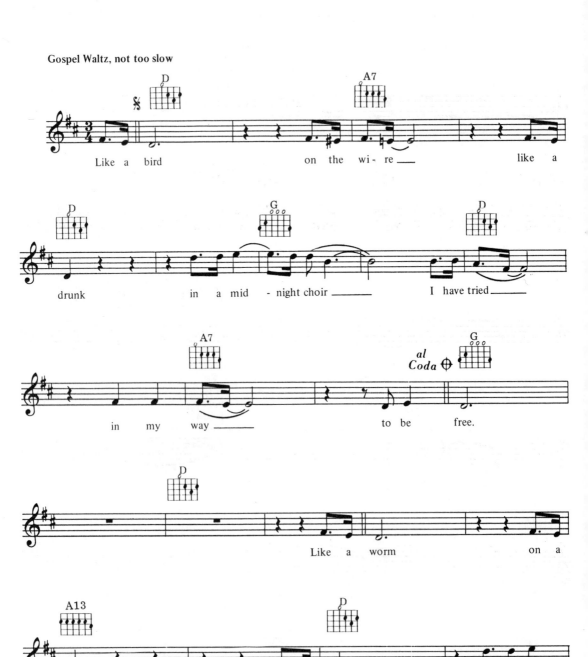

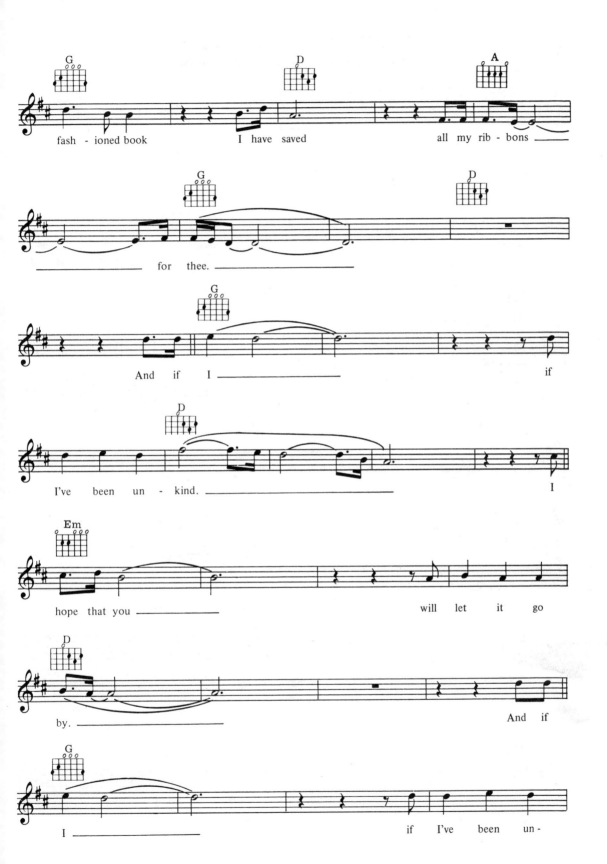

CODA

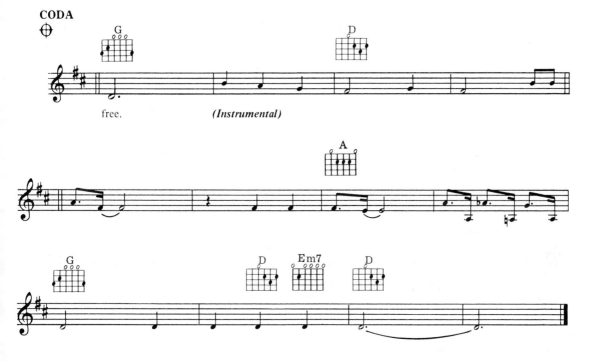

free.   *(Instrumental)*

Like a bird on the wire
Like a drunk in a midnight choir
I have tried in my way to be free
Like a worm on a hook
Like a knight from some old-fashioned book
I have saved all my ribbons for thee
    If I have been unkind
    I hope that you can just let it go by
    If I have been untrue,
    I hope you know it was never to you.

Like a baby stillborn
Like a beast with his horn
I have torn everyone who reached out for me
But I swear by this song
And by all that I have done wrong
I will make it all up to thee.
    I saw a beggar leaning on his wooden crutch
    He said to me, "You must not ask for so much."
    And a pretty woman leaning in her darkened door,
    She cried to me, "Hey, why not ask for more?"

12
THE BLACK VELVET BAND
Irish Traditional

CHORUS

Her eyes, they spark-led like dia-monds, __ you'd think she was queen o' the land, ____ With her hair thrown o-ver her shoul-ders, tied up with a Black Vel-vet Band. ___

D.C.

(2) As I went waiking down broadway, not intending to stay very long,
I met with a frolicksome damsel as she came a tripping along.
A watch she pulled out of her pocket and slipped it right into my hand,
On the very first day that I met her: bad luck to the Black Velvet Band.
CHORUS

(3) Before the judge and the jury the both of us had to appear,
And a gentleman swore to the jewellery - the case against us was clear.
For seven years transportation right unto Van Dieman's Land,
Far away from my friends and relations to follow her Black Velvet Band.
CHORUS

(3) Oh, all you brave young Irish lads, a warning take by me,
Beware of the pretty young damsels that are roamin' in Tralee.
They'll treat you to whiskey and porter until you're unable to stand,
And before you have time for to leave them, you are unto Van Dieman's Land.
CHORUS

BLOWIN' IN THE WIND
Words & Music by Bob Dylan

Moderato

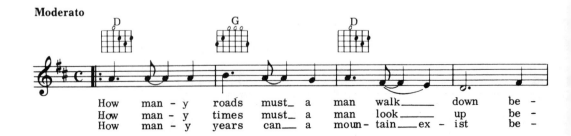

How man - y roads must_ a man walk_____ down be -
How man - y times must_ a man look_____ up be -
How man - y years can_ a moun - tain_ex - ist be -

fore you call him_ a man?_____ Yes,_ 'n'
fore he_ can see the_ the sky?_____ Yes,_ 'n'
fore it's washed to_ the sea?_____ Yes?_ 'n'

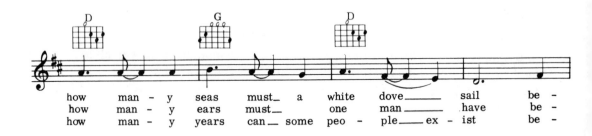

how man - y seas must_ a white dove_____ sail be -
how man - y ears must_ one man_____ have be -
how man - y years can_ some peo - ple_____ex - ist be -

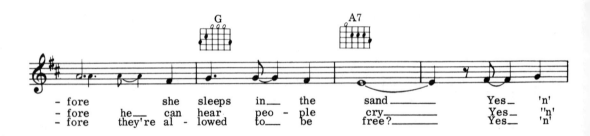

- fore she sleeps in_ the sand_____ Yes_ 'n'
- fore he_ can hear peo - ple cry?_____ Yes_ 'n'
- fore they're al - lowed to_ be free?_____ Yes_ 'n'

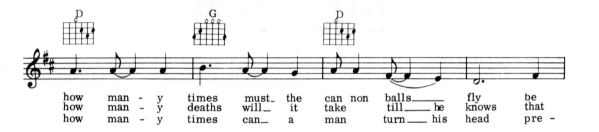

how man - y times must_ the can non balls____ fly be
how man - y deaths will_ it take till____ he knows that
how man - y times can_ a man turn____ his head pre -

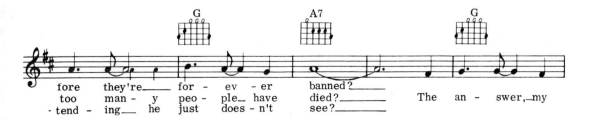

fore they're____ for - ev - er banned?_____
too man - y peo - ple_ have died?_____ The an - swer,_my
-tend - ing___ he just does - n't see?_____

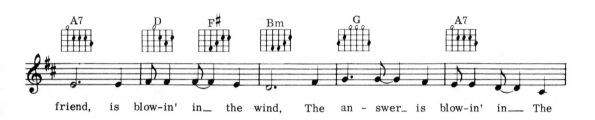

friend, is blow-in' in_ the wind, The an - swer_ is blow-in' in__ The

wind_____ wind._____ The an - swer_ is

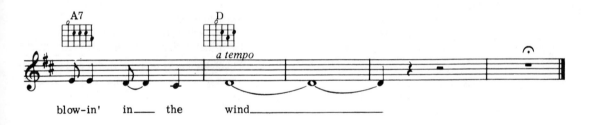

blow-in' in__ the wind_____

BARBARA ALLEN
Traditional

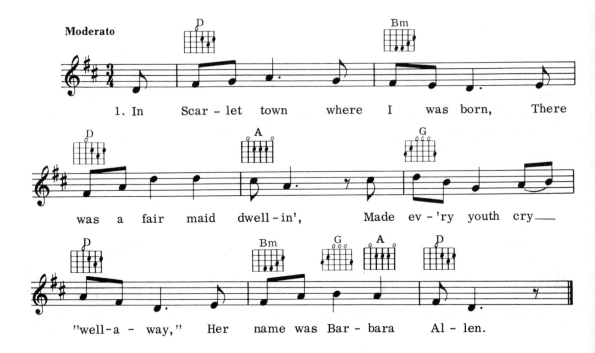

Moderato

1. In Scar-let town where I was born, There
was a fair maid dwell-in', Made ev-'ry youth cry—
"well-a-way," Her name was Bar-bara Al-len.

2. All in the merry month of May
   When green buds they were swellin',
   Young Jimmy Grove on his deathbed lay
   For love of Barbara Allen.

3. He sent his man unto her then,
   To the place where she was dwellin',
   To bring her to poor Jimmy Grove,
   The lovely Barbara Allen.

4. And death was printed on his face,
   And o'er his heart was stealin',
   Before she came to comfort him,
   The willful Barbara Allen.

5. So slowly, slowly she came up,
   And slowly she came nigh him,
   And all she said, when there she came,
   "Young man, I think you're dying."

6. He said, "I am a dying man,
   One kiss from you will cure me."
   "One kiss from me you will never get,"
   Said cruel Barbara Allen.

7. As she was walking o'er the fields,
   She heard the death bells knellin',
   And every peal did again reveal
   How cruel Barbara Allen.

8. When he was dead and in his grave,
   Her heart was struck with sorrow,
   "Oh, mother, mother make my bed,
   For I shall die tomorrow."

9. And on her deathbed as she lay,
   She begged a place beside him,
   And sore repented of that day
   That she did e'er deny him.

10. "Farewell," she said, "ye virgins all,
    And shun the fault I fell in,
    Henceforth take warning by the fall
    Of heartless Barbara Allen."

11. Then she was buried on the moor,
    And he was laid beside her,
    Above his grave red roses grew,
    Above hers, a green briar.

15
BLOW THE MAN DOWN
Traditional

Rhythmically

G

1. Come___ all ye young fel - lows that fol - low the
2. On ___ board the Black Bal - ler I first served my

C   D7

sea, With a yeo - ho! We'll blow the man down! And
time, With a yeo - ho! We'll blow the man down! And

Am   D7   C

please pay at - ten - tion and lis - ten to me,
in the Black Bal - ler I wast - ed my time,

G   D7   G

Give us some time to blow the man down!
Give us some time to blow the man down!

3. There were tinkers and tailors and sailors and all,
   With a yeo-ho! We'll blow the man down!
   That shipped for good seamen on board the Black Ball,
   Give us some time to blow the man down!

4. 'Tis larboard and starboard, you jump to the call,
   With a yeo-ho! We'll blow the man down!
   When Kicking Jack Williams commands the Black Ball.
   Give us some time to blow the man down!

BONNY MARY OF ARGYLE
Traditional

I have heard the ma-vis sing-ing___ His

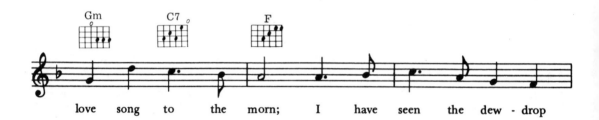

love song to the morn; I have seen the dew-drop

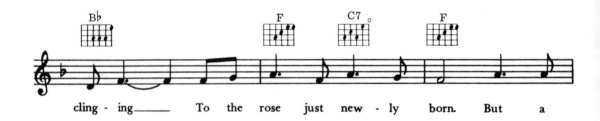

cling-ing___ To the rose just new-ly born. But a

sweet-er song has cheer'd me At the ev-'ning's gen-tle

close And I've seen an eye still bright-er Than the

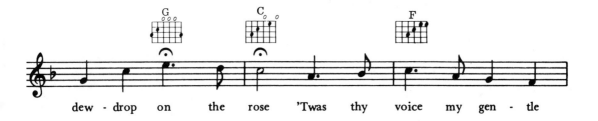

dew - drop on the rose 'Twas thy voice my gen - tle

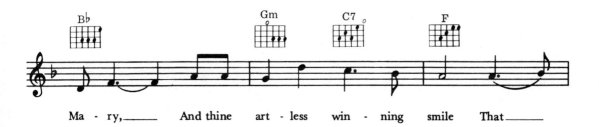

Ma - ry,_____ And thine art - less win - ning smile That_____

made this world an E - den, Bon - ny Ma - ry of__ Ar - gyle.

2. Tho' thy voice may lose its sweetness
   And thine eye its brightness too,
   Tho' thy step may lack its fleetness,
   And thy hair its sunny hue,
   Still to me wilt thou be dearer,
   Than all the world shall own.
   I have loved thee for thy beauty
   But not for that alone.
   I have sought thy heart, dear Mary,
   And its goodness was the wile
   That has made thee mine forever
   Bonny Mary of Argyle.

FROM BOTH SIDES NOW

Words & Music by Joni Mitchell

Moderately

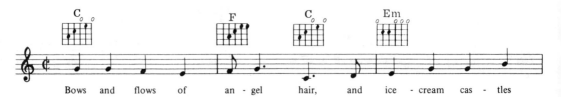

Bows and flows of an-gel hair, and ice-cream cas-tles

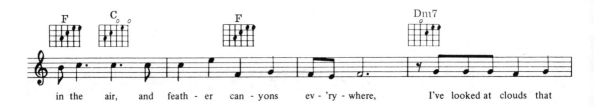

in the air, and feath-er can-yons ev-'ry-where, I've looked at clouds that

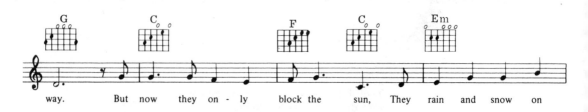

way. But now they on-ly block the sun, They rain and snow on

ev-'ry-one. So man-y things I would have done, But clouds got in my

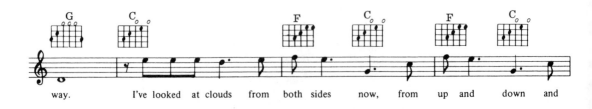

way. I've looked at clouds from both sides now, from up and down and

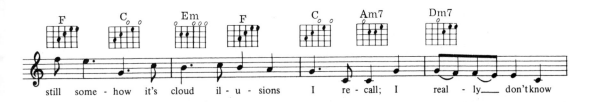

still some - how it's cloud il - u - sions I re - call; I real - ly___ don't know

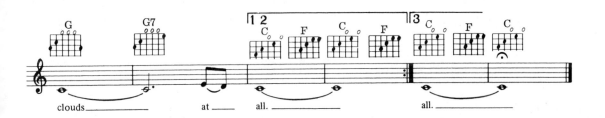

clouds_____ at ___ all. _____ all. _____

2 Moons and Junes and ferris wheels,
   The dizzy, dancing way you feel;
   When every fairy tale comes real,
   I've looked at love that way.
   But now it's just another show
   You leave 'em laughing when you go;
   And if you care, don't let them know,
   Don't give yourself away.

Chorus:
   I've looked at love from both sides now,
   From win and lose, and still somehow,
   It's love's illusions I recall,
   I really don't know love at all.

3 Tears and fears and feeling proud,
   To say I love you right out loud;
   Dreams and schemes and circus crowds,
   I've looked at life that way.
   But now old friends are acting strange,
   They shake their heads, they say I've changed;
   Well, something's lost and something's gained
   In living every day.

Chorus:
   I've looked at life from both sides now,
   From win and lose, and still somehow,
   It's life's illusions I recall,
   I really don't know life at all.

18
CALIFORNIA DREAMING
Words & Music by John Phillips

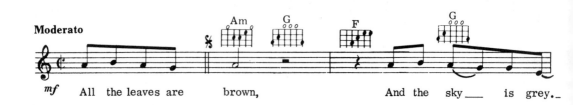

Moderato

mf All the leaves are brown, And the sky__ is grey.__

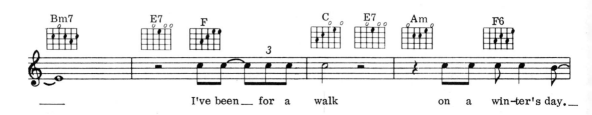

__ I've been__ for a walk on a win-ter's day.__

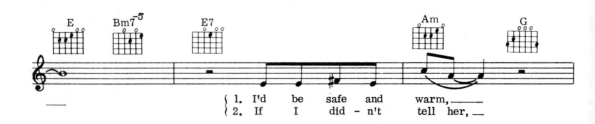

1. I'd be safe and warm,____
2. If I did-n't tell her,__

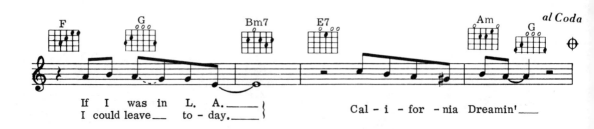

If I was in L. A.____
I could leave__ to-day.____

Cal-i-for-nia Dreamin'____

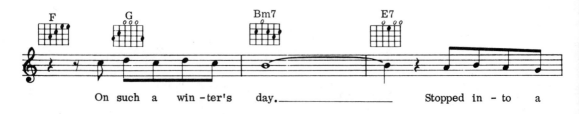

On such a win-ter's day._____ Stopped in-to a

CARELESS LOVE
Traditional

Moderato

Love, oh, love___ oh care - less love. Love, oh,

love oh care - less love Love, oh, love, oh, care - less

love. You see what love___ has done to me.

2 I love my mama and papa too, (3)
I'd leave them both to go with you.

3 What, oh what, will mama say, (3)
When she learns I've gone astray.

4 Once I wore my apron low, (3)
I couldn't scarcely keep you from my door.

5 Now my apron strings don't pin, (3)
You pass my door and you don't come in.

6 Don't you marry a railroad man (2)
A railroad man will kill you if he can,
And he'll drink your blood, drink it like wine.

COCKLES AND MUSSELS
Traditional

Moderately

1. In Dub-lin's fair ci-ty, where girls are so pret-ty, I first set my eyes on sweet Mol-ly Ma-lone, As she wheeled her wheel-bar-row through streets broad and nar-row, Cry-ing "Cock-les and muss-els a-live a-live o!"

CHORUS "A-live, a-live o!" A-live, a-live o!" Cry-ing "Cock-les and muss-els a-live, a-live o!" 2. She -live, a-live o!"

2. She was a fishmonger, but sure 'twas no wonder,
For so were her father and mother before;
And they each wheeled their barrow through streets broad and narrow,
Crying "Cockles and mussels alive, alive o!"

3. She died of a fever, and no one could save her,
And that was the end of sweet Molly Malone;
Her ghost wheels her barrow through streets broad and narrow,
Crying "Cockles and mussels alive, alive o!"

CAROLINA IN MY MIND
Words & Music by James Taylor

Kar- in she's ___ a sil - ver sun,_you'd best walk ___ her a - way and watch it shine. ___
Dark and si - lent late last night,_ I think I might have heard the high-way call.

Watch her watch _____ the morn-ing come. _____ A
Geese in flight _____ and dogs that bite. _____ And

sil - ver tear ___ ap - pear - ing now I'm cry - ing ain't I? I'm
signs that might ___ be o - mens say I'm go - ing, go - ing, I'm

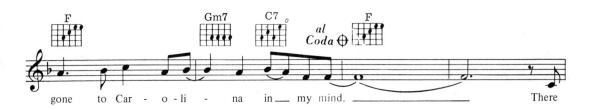

gone to Car - o - li - na in ___ my mind. _____ There

ain't no doubt no _____ ones mind ___ that love's ___ the fin - est thing ___ a - round. ___

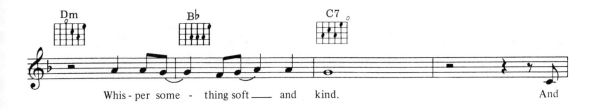

Whis - per some - thing soft ___ and kind. And

hey, babe, the sky's on fire, I'm dy - ing, ain't I? I'm

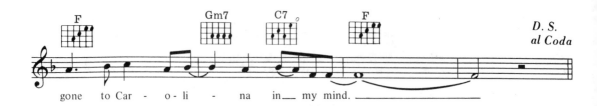

D. S.
al Coda

gone to Car - o - li - na in my mind.

CODA

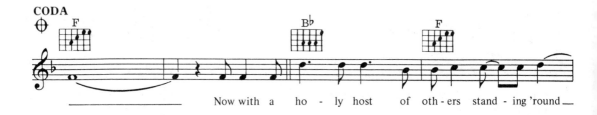

Now with a ho - ly host of oth - ers stand - ing 'round

me no, Still I'm on the dark side of the

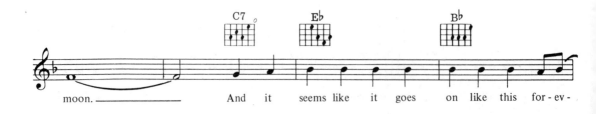

moon. And it seems like it goes on like this for - ev -

- er, you must for - give me.

CATCH THE WIND
Words & Music by Donovan

CAT'S IN THE CRADLE

Words & Music by Harry Chapin & Sandy Chapin

Moderate Folk Style

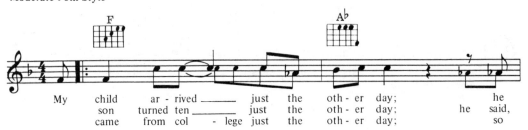

My child ar - rived _____ just the oth - er day; he
son turned ten _____ just the oth - er day; he said,
came from col - lege just the oth - er day; so

came to the world in the u - su - al way. _____ But there were
Thanks for the ball, Dad, come on lets play. _____ Can you
much like a man I just had to say, _____ "Son, I'm

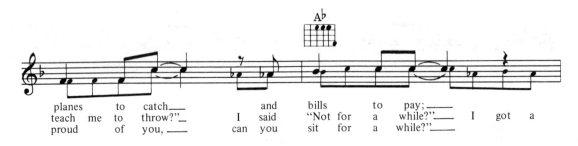

planes to catch_____ and bills to pay; _____ I
teach me to throw?"_____ I said "Not for a while?" _____ I got a
proud of you, _____ can you sit for a while?" _____

he learned to walk while I was a - way. _____ And he was
lot to do." He said, "That's o - kay." _____ And he,
He shook his head and he said with a smile, _____ "What I'd

My
Well, he

3. (Instrumental)

I've

long since re-tired, my son's moved a-way; I called him up just the oth-er day. I said "I'd like to see ___ you if you don't mind."___ He said, "I'd love to, Dad,___ if I can find the time.___

you see, my new job's a has-sle and the kids have the flu,___ but it's

(Instrumental)

24
BLOW THE WIND SOUTHERLY
Traditional

CLEMENTINE
Traditional

Moderato

1. In a ca - vern, in a can - yon, Ex - ca - va - ting for a mine, dwelt a mi - ner, for - ty ni - ner and his daugh - ter Cle - men - tine.

Oh my dar - ling, oh my dar - ling, oh my dar - ling Cle - men - tine, Thou are lost and gone for e - ver, dread-ful sor - ry Cle - men - tine. *D.C.*

2. Light she was and like a fairy,
   And her shoes were number nine,
   Herring boxes without topses,
   Sandals were for Clementine.
   Chorus

3. Drove she ducklings to the water,
   Ev'ry morning just at nine,
   Hit her foot against a splinter,
   Fell into the foaming brine.
   Chorus

4. Ruby lips above the water,
   Blowing bubbles soft and fine,
   But alas I was no swimmer,
   So I lost my Clementine.
   Chorus

5. In a churchyard, near the canyon
   Where the myrtle doth entwine,
   There grow roses, pretty roses,
   Fertilized by Clementine.
   Chorus

6. Then the miner, forty niner,
   Soon began to peak and pine,
   Thought he "oughter jine" his daughter,
   Now he's with his Clementine.
   Chorus

7. In my dreams she still doth haunt me,
   Robed in garments soaked with brine,
   Though in life I used to hug her,
   Now she's dead I draw the line.
   Chorus

8. Now ye boy scouts, heed the warning,
   In this tragic tale of mine,
   Artificial respiration,
   Would have saved my Clementine.
   Chorus

9. How I missed her, how I missed her,
   How I missed my Clementine,
   Till I kissed her little sister,
   And forgot my Clementine.
   Chorus

COLOURS

Words & Music by Donovan

1. Yel-low is the col-our of my true love's hair in the
2. Green's the col-our of the spark-lin' corn in the
3. Mel-low is the feel-in' that I get when I

morn-in' When we rise in the
morn-in' When we rise in the
see her Mm hmm when I

morn-in' when we rise
morn-in' when we rise That's the
see her uh - huh That's the

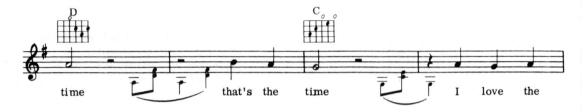

time that's the time I love the

best.

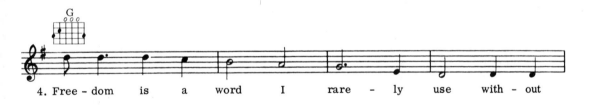

4. Free - dom is a word I rare - ly use with - out

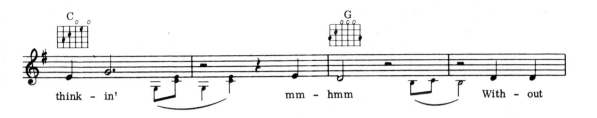

think - in' mm - hmm With - out

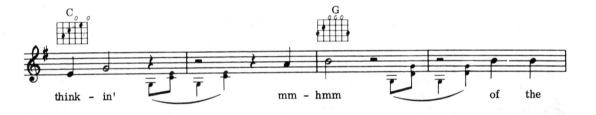

think - in' mm - hmm of the

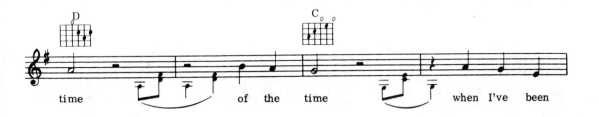

time of the time when I've been

loved.

COTTONFIELDS
Words & Music by Huddie Ledbetter

DON'T THINK TWICE, IT'S ALL RIGHT

Words & Music by Bob Dylan

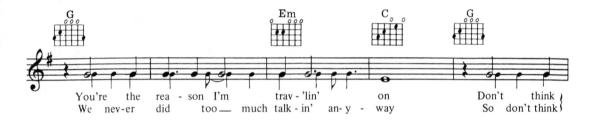

You're the rea - son I'm trav - 'lin' on   Don't think
We nev-er did too— much talk - in' an- y - way   So don't think

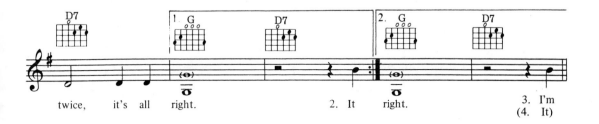

twice, it's all right.   2. It right.   3. I'm
                                                         (4. It)

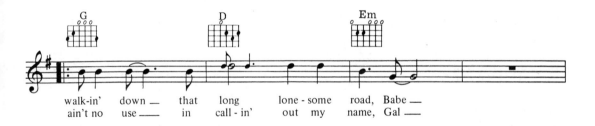

walk-in' down — that long lone - some road, Babe —
ain't no use — in call - in' out my name, Gal —

Where I'm bound I can't — tell   But
Like you nev - er did be - fore   It

good - bye's   too good a word, Gal —
ain't no use —   in call - in' out my name, Gal —

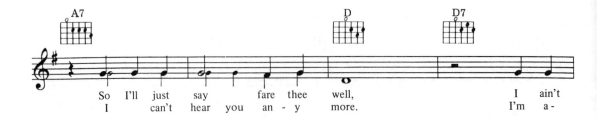

So I'll just say   fare thee   well,   I   ain't
I   can't   hear   you   an - y   more.   I'm a-

say - in'   you   treat - ed   me   un - kind   You
think - in'   and   a -   won - d'rin   all   the   way   down   the   road   I

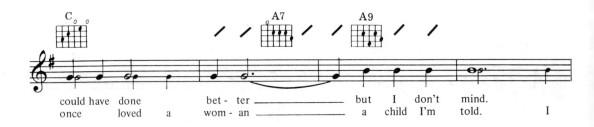

could have   done   bet - ter _____   but   I   don't   mind.
once   loved   a   wom - an _____   a   child   I'm   told.   I

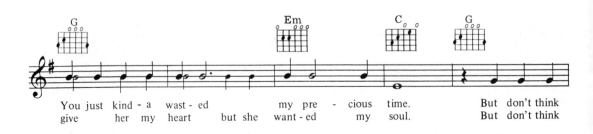

You   just   kind - a   wast - ed   my   pre - cious   time.   But   don't think
give   her   my   heart   but   she   want - ed   my   soul.   But   don't think

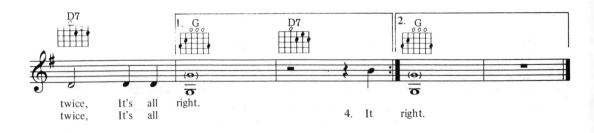

twice,   It's   all   right.
twice,   It's   all   4.   It   right.

COUNTRY ROAD
Words & Music by James Taylor

Slowly

Take — to the high-way won't you lend me — your name —

Your way — and my way seem to be one and the same,

Ma-ma don't un-der-stand — it —— she wants to know where I've been. I'd

have to be some — kind of nat-ural born fool to want to pass that way a-gain — But you know I could
(2nd time) But I could be

feel it —
there Lord. — *(Instrumental)* On a coun-try road — *(Instrumental)*

Sail on — home to Je-sus won't you good girls — and boys? —

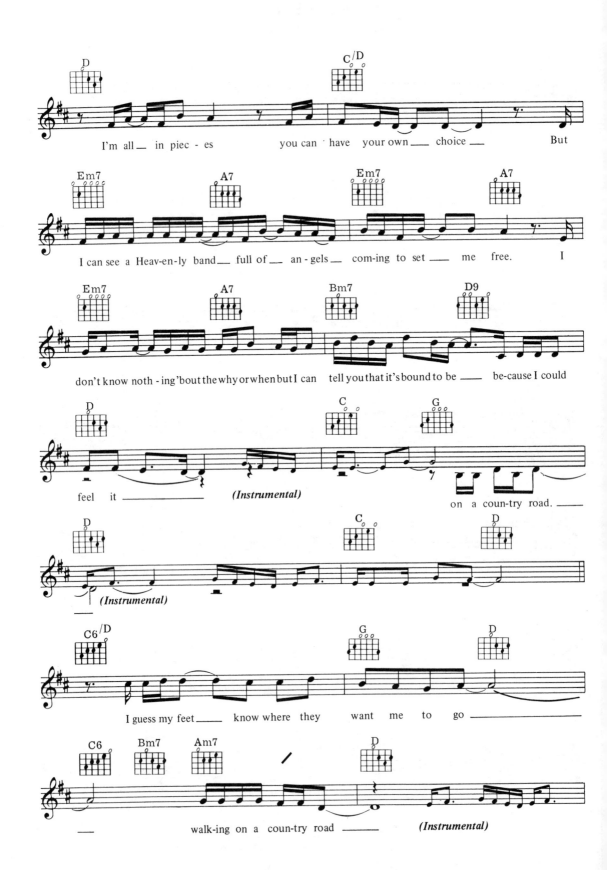

*D. C. al
Coda*

CODA

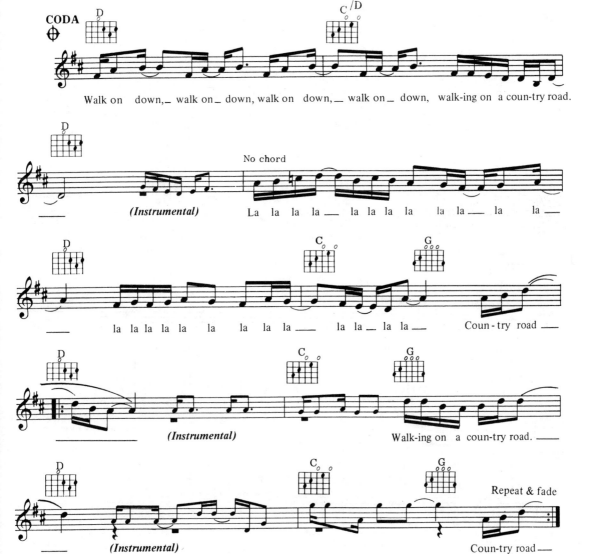

Walk on   down,__ walk on__ down, walk on   down,__ walk on__ down,   walk-ing on a coun-try road.

No chord

(Instrumental)   La   la   la   la __   la   la   la   la   la   la __   la   la __

__   la   la   la   la   la   la   la   la   la __   la   la __ la   la __   Coun-try road __

(Instrumental)   Walk-ing on   a coun-try road. __

Repeat & fade

(Instrumental)   Coun-try road __

30

DANNY BOY

Traditional Irish Melody
Words by Fred E. Weatherly

Oh, Dan-ny Boy, the pipes, the pipes are call - ing ____ from glen to

glen and down the moun - tain side. ____ The sum - mer's

gone, and all the ros - es fall - ing, ____ it's you, it's

you must go, and I must bide. ____ But come you back when sum-mer's in the

mea - dow, ____ Or when the val - ley's hushed and white with

snow. ____ It's I'll be here in sun - shine or in

sha - dow. ____ Oh, Dan - ny Boy, oh Dan - ny Boy, I love you

31
DOWN BY THE RIVERSIDE
Traditional

1. I'm gon - na lay down my sword and shield, down by the

riv - er-side,— down by the riv-er-side,— down by the

riv - er-side. I'm gon-na lay down my sword and shield, down by the

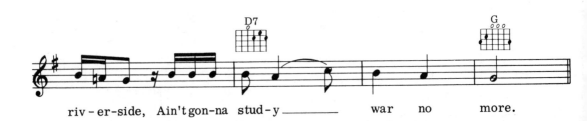

riv - er-side, Ain't gon-na stud-y _____ war no more.

Chorus

I ain't gon-na stud-y war no more, I ain't gon-na stud-y war no

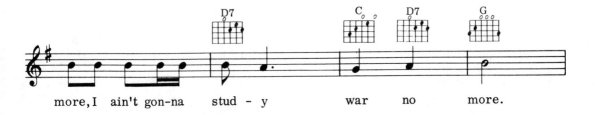

more, I ain't gon-na stud - y war no more.

I ain't gon-na stud-y war no more, I ain't gon-na stud-y war no

more, I ain't gon-na stud - y _____ war no more. _____

2. I'm gonna put on my long white robe, (etc.)

3. I'm gonna put on my starry crown, (etc.)

4. I'm gonna put on my angel shoes, (etc.)

5. I'm gonna ride on a horse with wings, (etc.)

6. I'm gonna follow the Prince of Peace, (etc.)

7. I'm gonna join with the Angel Band, (etc.)

EARLY ONE MORNING
Traditional

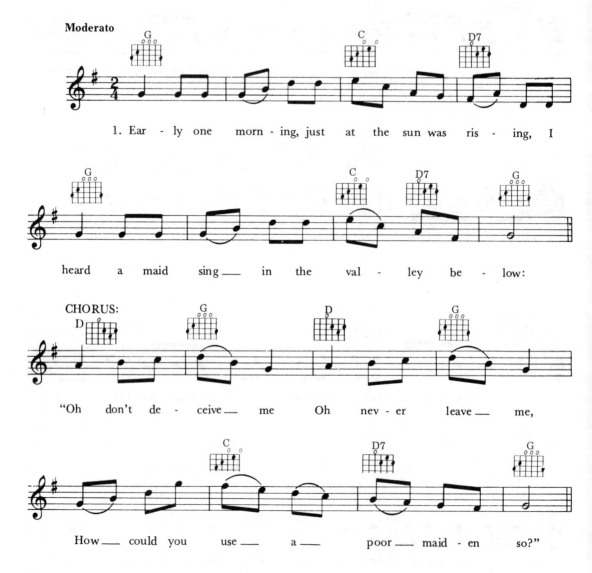

1. Ear - ly one morn - ing, just at the sun was ris - ing, I

heard a maid sing __ in the val - ley be - low:

CHORUS:

"Oh don't de - ceive __ me Oh nev - er leave __ me,

How __ could you use __ a __ poor __ maid - en so?"

2. "Gay is the garland and fresh are the roses
   I've culled from the garden to bind on thy brow;

CHORUS:

3. "Remember the vows that you made to your Mary,
   Remember the bow'r where you vow'd to be true;

CHORUS:

4. Thus sung the poor maiden, her sorrow bewailing,
   Thus sung the poor maid in the valley below:

ENGLAND
Words & Music by Ralph McTell

Moderato

(Instrumental)

1. What is it a-bout you makes me feel this way?
3. (See block lyric)

When I'm leav-ing you when I'm com-ing home I'm lost for words — to say, — and I

know your faults — and fail - ures and the troub-les that you've been through. But it's

more a-bout — what hap-pens now ___ and what we're com - ing to. And the

e - cho ____ from the green hills runs through her ci - ty streets, — and the

sun that shines on Eng - land well it lifts the heart ___ in me.

VERSES 2 & 4

2. What is it a - bout you that took men in - to war?___
4. (See block lyric)

Rows and rows ___ of cros - ses: who re-mem-bers why what for?

The cor- ners ___ of these foreign fields, ___ the dust in them ___ con - cealed,

out of sight ___ but not out of mind, ___ don't you know that Eng-land feels?___ And the

e - cho ___ from the green hills ___ runs through the ci - ty streets, ─ the rain

that falls on Eng - land well it wa-shes care ___ from me.

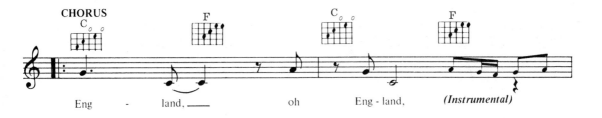

CHORUS

Eng - land, ____ oh Eng - land, *(Instrumental)*

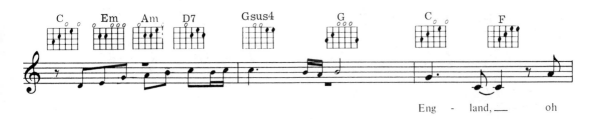

Eng - land, ____ oh

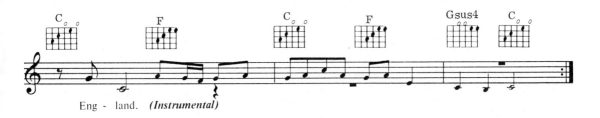

Eng - land. *(Instrumental)*

3.   Don't make this out a battle hymn or
        a song for victory,
    It's just a way to try to say
    What England means to me.
    And our accents and our colours change
    From the city to the farmland,
    From the moorland to the mountain,
        from the river to the sea.

    And the echo from the green hills
    Runs through her city streets,
    And the wind that blows through England
    Breathes its life in you and me.

    England, oh England,
    Oh England, oh England.

4.   From the rolling road to the winding lane,
        from the field to factory,
    From summer's haze to winter's glaze,
    And all the colours inbetween,
    It's a stillness in the evening,
    It's the heartbeat that I'm feeling,
    From Cornwall to Northumberland,
        from the Pennines to the sea.

    And the echo from the green hills
    Runs through the city streets,
    And the wind that blows through England
    Breathes its life in you and me.

    England, oh England,
    Oh England, oh England.

34

FIRE AND RAIN
Words & Music by James Taylor

Moderato

Verse:

Just yes-ter-day morn-in' they let me know___ you were gone,___

Su-san, the plans they made put an end to you. I walked out this morn-in' and I

wrote down this song,___ I just can't re-mem-ber who to send it to.

Chorus:

I've seen fire and I've seen rain, I seen sun-ny days___ that I thought would nev-er

end,   I seen   lone - ly times___ when   I   could not   find   a   friend,___

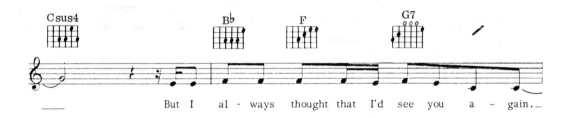

___   But   I   al - ways   thought that I'd   see   you   a   –   gain.___

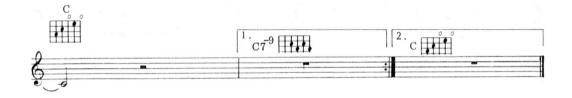

Verse 2.   Won't you look down upon me, Jesus, you got to help me make a stand
                 You just got to see me through another day
                 My body's achin' and my time is at hand
                 An' I won't make it any other way.   (Chorus)

      3.   Been walkin' my mind to an easy time, my back turned towards the sun
                 Lord knows when the cold wind blows it'll turn your head around
                 Well, there's hours of time on the telephone line, to talk about things to come
                 Sweet dreams and flying machines in pieces on the ground.   (Chorus)

35

THE FOGGY FOGGY DEW
Traditional

Moderato

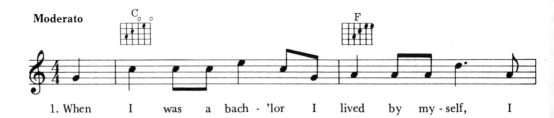

1. When I was a bach-'lor I lived by my-self, I

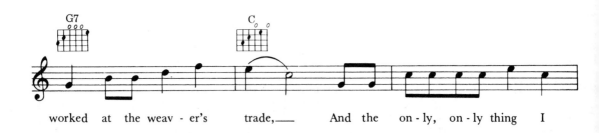

worked at the weav-er's trade,— And the on-ly, on-ly thing I

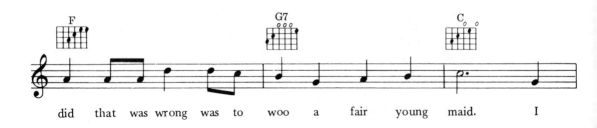

did that was wrong was to woo a fair young maid. I

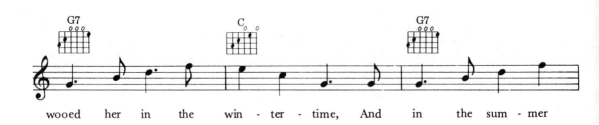

wooed her in the win-ter-time, And in the sum-mer

too,   And the   on - ly, on - ly, thing   I   did   that was wrong was to

keep   her   from   the   fog - gy,   fog - gy   dew.

2. One night she knelt close by my side
   As I lay fast asleep.
   She threw her arms around my neck,
   And then began to weep.
   She wept, she cried, she tore her hair,
   Ah me, what could I do?
   So all night long I held her in my arms
   Just to keep her from the foggy, foggy dew.

3. Oh, I am a bachelor, I live with my son,
   We work at the weaver's trade.
   And every single time I look into his eyes
   He reminds me of the fair young maid.
   He reminds me of the winter time,
   And of the summer too.
   And the many, many times I held her in my arms
   Just to keep her from the foggy, foggy dew.

36

FOUR DRUNKEN NIGHTS

Traditional

Moderato

1. I came home the oth - er night as drunk as I could be, And I saw a horse in the sta - ble where my horse ought to be, So I said to my wife, my pret - ty lit - tle wife, "Ex - plain this thing to me, What can this horse be do - ing here where my horse ought to be?" "You darn fool, you drunk - en fool, can't you e - ven see? It's noth - ing but a

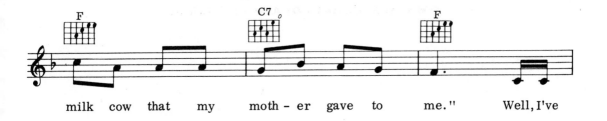

milk cow that my moth - er gave to me." Well, I've

trav-eled this world o - ver, ten thou-sand miles or more, But a

sad-dle on a milk cow I nev-er did see be - fore.

2. I came home the next night as drunk as I could be,
   And there hung a hat on the hat rack where my hat ought to be,
   So I said to my wife, my pretty little wife, "Explain this thing to me,
   What can this hat be doing here where my hat ought to be?"

   "You darn fool, you drunken fool, can't you even see?
   It's nothing but a thundermug my granny sent to me. "
   Well, I've traveled this world over, ten thousand miles or more,
   But a J. B. Stetson thundermug I never did see before.

3. I came home the third night as drunk as I could be,
   I saw some pants draped on the chair where my pants ought to be,
   So I said to my wife, my pretty little wife, "Explain this thing to me,
   What can these pants be doing here where my pants ought to be?"

   "You darn fool, you drunken fool, can't you even see?
   It's nothing but a bedspread your mother gave to me."
   Well, I've traveled this world over, ten thousand miles or more,
   But a zipper on a bedspread I never did see before.

4. I came home the fourth night as drunk as I could be.
   I saw a head on the pillow where my head ought to be,
   So I said to my wife, my pretty little wife, "Explain this thing to me,
   What can that head be doing there where my head ought to be?"

   "You darn fool, you drunken fool, can't you even see?
   It's nothing but a cabbage my mother sent to me."
   Well, I've traveled this wide world over, ten thousand miles or more,
   But a mustache on a cabbage I never did see before.

GALWAY BAY

Words & Music by Dr Arthur Colahan

38

GREENSLEEVES
Traditional

1. A - las, my love,— you do me wrong— To cast me out— dis -

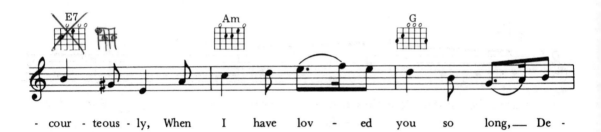

- cour - teous - ly, When I have lov - ed you so long,— De -

- light - ing in— your com - pa - ny. Green - sleeves— was

CHORUS

my de - light,— Green - sleeves was my heart of gold. Green - sleeves was my

D. C.

la - dy love,— And who but my la - dy Green - sleeves.

2. I have been ready at your hand
   To grant whatever you would crave;
   I have both wagered life and land,
   Your love and good will for to have.

   CHORUS

3. I bought thee kerchiefs to thy head
   That were wrought fine and gallantly;
   I kept thee both at board and bed,
   Which cost my purse well favoredly.

   CHORUS

4. Thy smock of gold so crimson red,
   With pearls bedecked sumptuously.
   The like no other lasses had,
   And yet thou wouldest not love me.

   CHORUS

5. Thy gown was of the grassy green,
   Thy sleeves of satin hanging by;
   Which made thee be our harvest queen,
   And yet thou wouldest not love me.

   CHORUS

6. Thou couldst desire no earthly thing,
   But still thou hadst it readily;
   Thy music still to play and sing,
   And yet thou wouldest not love me.

   CHORUS

7. Well, I will pray to God on high
   That thou my constancy mayst see;
   And that yet once before I die
   Thou wilt vouchsafe to love me.

   CHORUS

8. Greensleeves, now farewell, adieu!
   God I pray to prosper thee;
   For I am still thy lover true -
   Come once again and love me.

   CHORUS

39

GUANTANAMERA
Words by Jose Marti
Music Adaptation by Hector Angulo and Pete Seeger

Moderato

Guan-ta-na-me-ra   gua-ji-ra Guan-ta-na-me-ra

Guan-ta-na-me - ra   gua-ji-ra Guan-ta-na-me - ra!   ra!

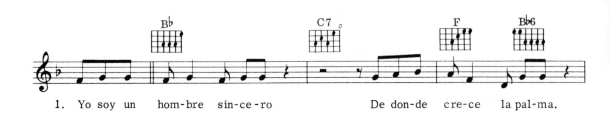

1. Yo soy un hom-bre sin-ce-ro   De don-de cre-ce la pal-ma.

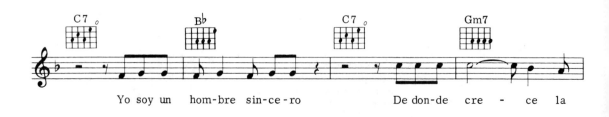

Yo soy un hom-bre sin-ce-ro   De don-de cre - ce la

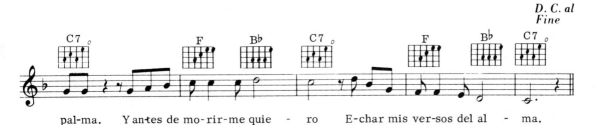

pal-ma. Y an-tes de mo-rir-me quie - ro E-char mis ver-sos del al - ma.

2. Mi verso es de un verde claro,
    Y de un carmin encendido.
    Mi verso es de un verde claro,
    Y de un carmin encendido.
    Mi verso es un cierro herido
    Que busca en el monte amparo.
       [Chorus]

3. Con los pobres de la tierra
    Quiero yo mi suerte echar.
    Con los pobres de la tierra
    Quiero yo mi suerte echar.
    El arroyo de la sierra
    Me complace mas que el mar.
       [Chorus]

Literal translation:

1. I am a truthful man from the land
    of palm trees.
    Before dying I want to share these
    poems of my soul.

2. My poems are light green,
    but they are also flaming crimson.
    My verses are like a wounded faun
    seeking refuge in the forest.

3. With the poor people of this earth
    I want to share my fate.
    The little streams of the mountains
    please me more than the sea.

40
THE GYPSY ROVER
Words & Music by Leo Maguire

Andante Moderato

(1) The gyp - sy ro - ver came o - ver the hill,

Down thro' the val - ley so sha - dy, He whist-led and sang till the

green-woods rang, And he won the heart of a la - -

CHORUS

- dy. Ah de doo ah de doo da day,

Ah de doo ah de day de, He whist-led and sang till the

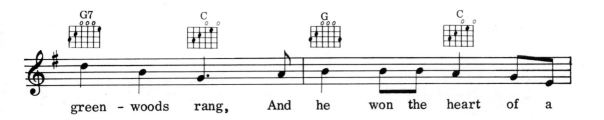

green - woods rang, And he won the heart of a

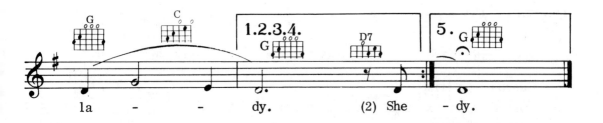

la - - dy. (2) She - dy.

(2) She left her father's castle gate,
She left her fair young lover,
She left her servants and her state,
To follow the gypsy rover.

(3) Her father saddled up his fastest steed,
He ranged the valleys over,
He sought his daughter at great speed,
And the whistling gypsy rover.

(4) He came at last to a mansion fine,
Down by the river Clady,
And there was music and there was wine,
For the gypsy and his lady.

(5) "He is no gypsy, father dear,
But lord of these lands all over,
I'm going to stay 'til my dying day,
With my whistling gypsy rover."

41

HALLELUJAH, I'M A BUM
Traditional

Moderato — F

1. Oh, why don't I work like oth-er men do? Tell me,

how can I work when there's no work to do?

Chorus F

Hal-le-lu-jah, I'm a bum, hal-le-lu-jah, bum a-gain! Hal-le-

F — C7 — F

lu-jah, give us a hand-out to re-vive us a-gain.

2. Now, I don't like work, and work don't like me,
   And that is the reason that I'm so hungry.

3. I went to a house and I knocked on the door,
   The lady said, "Go, Bum, you've been here before!"

4. I knocked on a door and asked for some bread,
   But the lady there told me the baker was dead.

5. I went to a bar and asked for a drink,
   They said, "Out in back there's a glass by the sink!"

6. When springtime does come, won't we have a time?
   We'll go on the bum and we won't need a dime,

7. I passed a saloon and I looked in the door,
   And there lay the bartender asleep on the floor.

8. I poured me a drink, then I poured me ten more,
   Then I joined the bartender and started to snore.

9. The next thing I knew I was headed for jail
   Without any money, without any bail.

10. The next day in court the judge said to me,
    "For the next 30 days in the jail-house you'll be!"

11. Now, springtime is here, and won't I have fun?
    I am free once again, and I'm back on the bum!

42
HE'S GOT THE WHOLE WORLD IN HIS HANDS
Traditional

HEY, THAT'S NO WAY
TO SAY GOODBYE

Words & Music by Leonard Cohen

Moderately

I loved you in the morn - ing, our kiss-es sweet and warm, _____ your

hair up - on the pil - low like a sleep - y gold - en storm; _____ Yes,

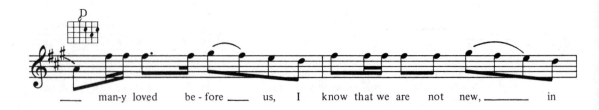

_____ man-y loved be - fore _____ us, I know that we are not new, _____ in

ci - ty and in for - est they smiled like me and you; _____ but

now it's come to dis - tan - ces and both of us must try; _____ Your

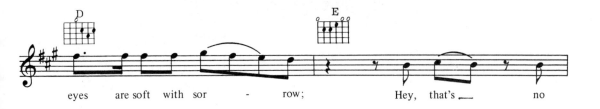

eyes   are soft   with   sor - row;   Hey,   that's __   no

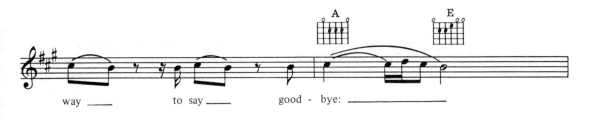

way __   to say __   good - bye: _____

(Instrumental)   2. I'm   not

2. I'm not looking for another
   As I wander in my time
   Walk me to the corner
   Our steps will always rhyme.
   You know my love goes with you
   As your love stays with me
   It's just the way it changes
   Like the shoreline and the sea.
   But let's not talk of love or chains
   And things we can't untie,
   Your eyes are soft with sorrow,
   Hey, that's no way to say goodbye.

3. I loved you in the morning
   Our kisses deep and warm
   Your hair upon the pillow
   Like a sleepy golden storm.
   Yes, many loved before us
   I know that we are not new
   In city and in forest
   They smiled like me and you.
   But let's not talk of love or chains
   And things we can't untie,
   Your eyes are soft with sorrow
   Hey, that's no way to say goodbye.

HURDY GURDY MAN
Words & Music by Donovan Leitch

I BELIEVE MY LOVE LOVES ME
Words & Music by Tom Paxton

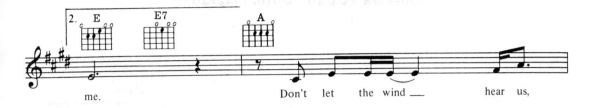

me.　　　　Don't let the wind ___ hear us,

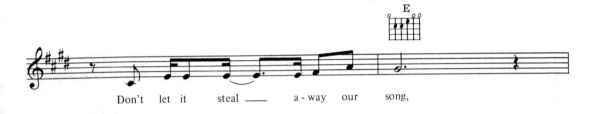

Don't let it steal ___ a - way our song,

Peo - ple would hear_ it, ___ they'd sing it and I know__ they'd get it

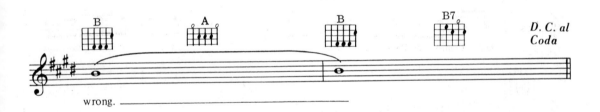

wrong. ___

me.　　　Feel ___ how it grows, I know__ how it goes,

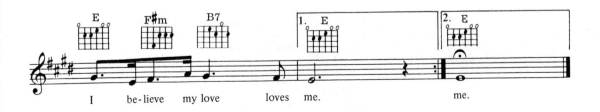

I be - lieve my love loves me.　　　me.

46
EARLY MORNIN' RAIN
Words & Music by Gordon Lightfoot

2 Out on runway number nine
Big seven-o-seven set to go,
Well, I'm stuck here on the grass,
Where the cold wind blows.
Well, the liquor tasted good,
And the time went fast.
Well, there she goes, my friend,
There she's rollin' now at last.

3 Hear the mighty engines roar,
See the silver bird on high,
She's away and westward bound
Far above the clouds she'll fly,
Where the mornin' rain don't fall
And the sun always shines.
She'll be flyin' o'er my home
In about three hours time.

4 We'll this old airport's got me down,
It ain't no earthly good to me,
'Cause I'm stuck here on the ground
As cold and drunk as I can be.
You can't jump a jet plane
Like you can a freight train,
So I best be on my way
In the early mornin' rain.

IF I HAD A HAMMER
Words & Music by Lee Hays & Pete Seeger

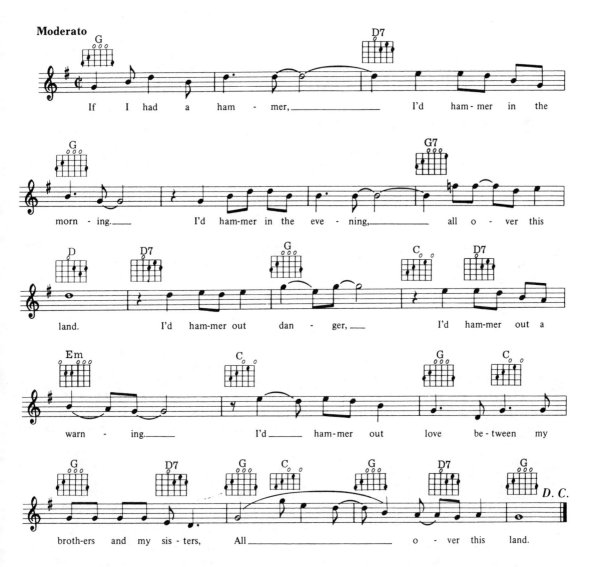

2 If I had a bell, I'd ring it in the morning
I'd ring it in the evening all over this land;
I'd ring out danger, I'd ring out a warning
I'd ring out love between my brothers and my sisters
All over this land.

3 If I had a song, I'd sing it in the morning
I'd sing it in the evening all over this land;
I'd sing out danger, I'd sing out a warning
I'd sing out love between my brothers and my sisters
All over this land.

4 Well I got a hammer and I got a bell
And I got a song to sing all over this land;
It's the hammer of justice, it's the bell of freedom
It's the song of love between my brothers and my sisters
All over this land.

IF YOU COULD READ MY MIND
Words & Music by Gordon Lightfoot

I'd walk a - way_____ like a mov-ie star_ who gets burned in a three-way script. En-ter num-ber two: A mov-ie queen to play the scene of bring-ing all the good things out of me. But for now, love, let's be real; I nev - er thought_ I could feel this way_ and I've got to say_ that I just don't get it. I don't know where we went wrong_ but the feel-in's gone_ and I

I Know Where I'm Goin'

Words & Music by Herbert Hughes

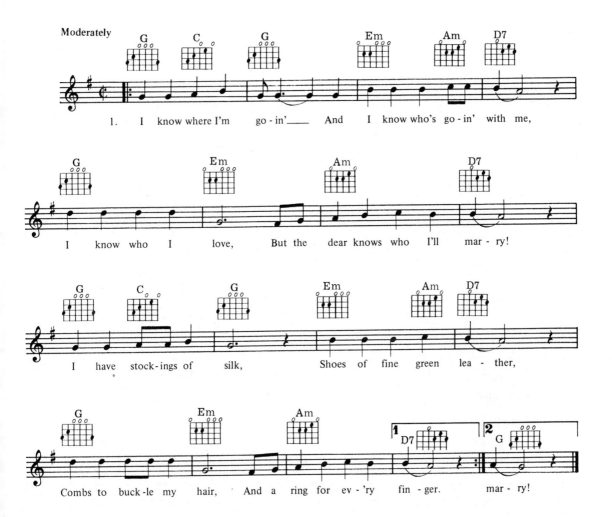

Moderately

1. I know where I'm go-in'___ And I know who's go-in' with me,
I know who I love, But the dear knows who I'll mar-ry!
I have stock-ings of silk, Shoes of fine green lea-ther,
Combs to buck-le my hair, And a ring for ev-'ry fin-ger. mar-ry!

2. Some say he's black,
But I say he's bonny,
The fairest of them all
My handsome winsome Johnny.
Feather beds are soft,
And painted rooms are bonny,
But I would leave them all
To go with my love Johnny.
I know where I'm goin',
And I know who's goin' with me,
I know who I love,
But the dear knows who I'll marry!

IT AIN'T ME, BABE
Words & Music by Bob Dylan

Moderately

1. Go 'way from my win - dow, _____ Leave at your

own cho - sen speed, _____ I'm not the one you

want, Babe, _____ I'm not the one you need. _____

You say you're look - in' for some - one _____ Nev - er weak but

al - ways strong, _____ To pro - tect you an' de -

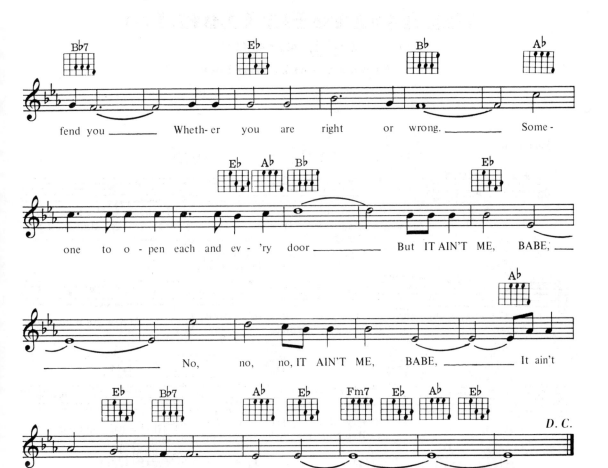

fend you _____ Wheth-er you are right or wrong. _____ Someone to o - pen each and ev - 'ry door _____ But IT AIN'T ME, BABE, __
_____ No, no, no, IT AIN'T ME, BABE, _____ It ain't
me you're look - in' for, Babe. _____

D. C.

2. Go lightly from the ledge Babe,
   Go lightly on the ground,
   I'm not the one you want, Babe,
   I will only let you down.
   You say you're looking for someone
   Who will promise never to part,
   Someone to close his eyes for you,
   Someone to close his heart.
   Someone who will die for you an' more
   But it ain't me, Babe,
   No, no, no it ain't me, Babe
   It ain't me you're looking for, Babe.

3. Go melt back into the nite Babe,
   Everything inside is made of stone,
   There's nothing in here moving
   An' anyway I'm not alone.
   You say you're looking for someone
   Who'll pick you up each time you fall,
   To gather flowers constantly
   An' to come each time you call.
   A lover for your life an' nothing more
   But it ain't me, Babe,
   No, no, no it ain't me, Babe,
   It ain't me you're looking for, Babe.

I'll Have To Say I Love You In A Song

Words & Music by Jim Croce

IT WAS A VERY GOOD YEAR
Words & Music by Ervin Drake

JEANIE WITH THE LIGHT BROWN HAIR

Words & Music by Stephen Foster

I dream of Jean-nie with the light brown hair,
I long for Jean-nie with the day - dawn smile,

Borne, like a va - pour, on the sum-mer's air; I see her trip-ping where the
Rad - iant in glad-ness, warm with win-ning guile; I hear her mel-o-dies, like

bright streams play, Hap-py as the dai - sies that dance on her way.
joys gone by, Sigh-ing round my heart o'er the fond hopes that die;

Man - y were the wild notes her mer-ry voice would pour, Man - y were the blithe birds that
Sigh-ing like the night wind and sob-bing like the rain, Wail-ing for the lost one that

war - bled them o'er; Ah! I dream of Jean-nie with the
comes not a - gain; Ah! I long for Jean-nie and my

light brown hair, Float-ing, like a va-pour, on the soft sum-mer air.
heart bows low, Nev - er more to find her where the bright wa-ters flow.

JENIFER JUNIPER
Words & Music by Donovan Leitch

Jen - i - fer,__ Jun - i - per,__ lives up - on the hill,__
Jen - i - fer,__ Jun - i - per,__ rides a dap - pled mare,__

Jen - i - fer,__ Jun - i - per,__ sit - ting ver - y still;__
Jen - i - fer,__ Jun - i - per,__ li - lacs in her hair;__

Is she sleep - ing? I__ don't think__ so, Is she breath - ing? Yes,__ ve - ry__ low,
Is she dream - ing? Yes,__ I think__ so, Is she pret - ty? Yes,__ ev - er__ so,

What-cha do - in', Jen - i - fer,__ my love?__ I'm think - ing of__
What-cha do - in', Jen - i - fer,__ my love?__

what it would be__ like if she loved me,__ You know just

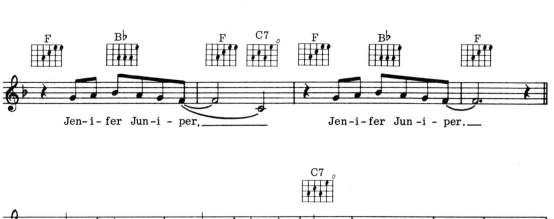

Jen-i-fer Jun-i-per,_____ Jen-i-fer Jun-i-per.__

Jen-i-fer,__ Jun-i-per,__ vit sur la col-line,__

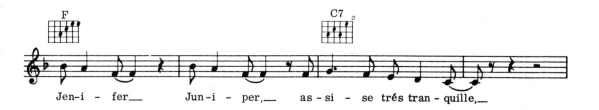

Jen-i-fer__ Jun-i-per,__ as-si-se trés tran-quille,__

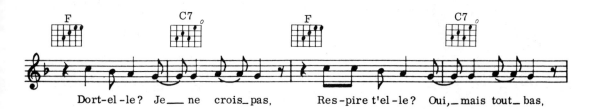

Dort-el-le? Je__ ne crois_pas, Res-pire t'el-le? Oui,__mais tout_ bas,

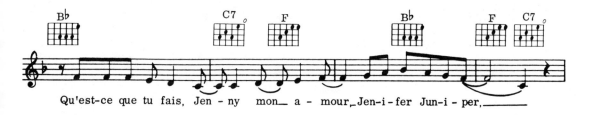

Qu'est-ce que tu fais, Jen-ny mon__ a-mour,_Jen-i-fer Jun-i-per,_____

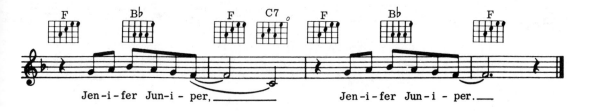

Jen-i-fer Jun-i-per,_____ Jen-i-fer Jun-i-per.__

55

JESSE
Words & Music by Janis Ian

Moderato

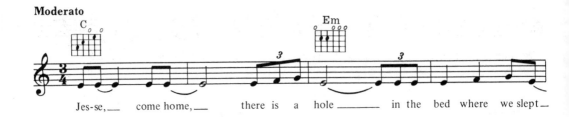

Jes-se,___ come home,___ there is a hole_____ in the bed where we slept___

___ Now it's grow-ing cold oh - Jes-sie ___ your

face in the place where we laid by the hearth ___ All a-part ___ it

hangs on my heart and I'm leav - ing the light on the stairs

No, I'm not scared ___ I'll wait for you oh Jes-

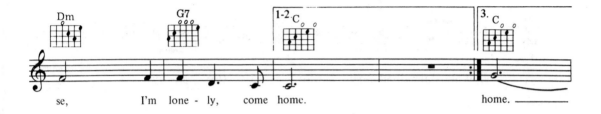

se, I'm lone - ly, come home. home. ___

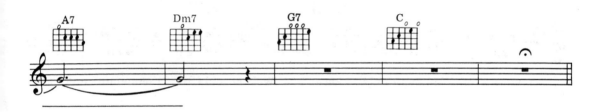

2. Jesse the floors and the paths recalling your steps
And I remember too,
All the pictures are fading and shading grey,
But I still set a place on the table at noon
And I'm leaving the light on the stairs,
No, I'm not scared, I'll wait for you
Oh Jesse, I'm lonely, come home.

3. Jesse, the 'spread on the bed
Is like when you left, I've kept it up for you.
And all the blues and the greens have been recently cleaned,
And it's seemingly new - hey Jesse me and you.
We'll swallow the light on the stairs
We'll do up my hair and sleep unaware
Hey, Jesse, I'm lonely, come home.

56

JOHN HENRY
Traditional

Moderato

1. When John Hen-ry was a lit-tle ba-by, ____

sit-tin' on his pap-py's knee, Well he picked up a ham-mer and a

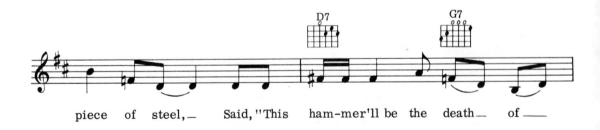

piece of steel, — Said, "This ham-mer'll be the death__ of ____

D. C.

me, oh Lord,— This ham-mer'll be the death__ of __ me."

2. Well, the captain said to John Henry, "Gonna bring that steam drill 'round,
   Gonna bring that steam drill out on the job,
   Gonna whup that steel on down, oh Lord,
   Gonna whup that steel on down."

3. John Henry then told the captain, "Bring that thirty pound hammer 'round,
   Thirty pound hammer with a twelve foot handle
   Gonna beat that steam drill down, oh Lord,
   Gonna beat that steam drill down."

4. "And I can tell you, captain, a man ain't nothin' but a man,
   But before I'd let that steam drill beat me down,
   I'd die with the hammer in my hand, oh Lord,
   Die with the hammer in my hand."

5. John Henry drove on down twenty feet, the hammer only drove nine,
   He drove so hard that he broke his heart,
   He laid down his hammer and died, oh Lord,
   Laid down his hammer and died.

6. They carried him off to the graveyard and buried him in the land,
   And every engine that goes racin' by
   Says "There's a real steel-drivin' man, oh Lord,
   There's a real steel-drivin' man."

57
JOHNNY TODD
Traditional

1. John - ny Todd he took a not - ion, For to cross the

rag - ing tide, _____ And he left his true

love be - hind him Weep - ing on the Li - ver - pool side.

2. For a week she wept full sorely,
   Tore her hair and wrung her hands
   Then she met with another sailor
   Walking on the Liverpool sands.

3. "Why fair maid, are you a-weeping
   For your Johnny gone to sea?
   If you will wed with me tomorrow,
   I will kind and constant be."

4. "I will buy you sheets and blankets
   I'll buy you a wedding ring,
   You will have a silver cradle,
   For to rock your babies in."

5. Johnny Todd came home from sailing
   Sailing o'er the ocean wide
   For to find that his fair and false one
   Was another sailor's bride.

6. So all young men who go a-sailing
   For to fight the foreign foe,
   Never leave your love, like Johnny,
   Marry her before you go.

58
THE KEEL ROW
Traditional

1. Oh, who is like my John - nie, Sae leish, sae blythe, sae
2. He has na mair o' learn - ing, Than tells his week - ly
3. He wears a blue bon - net, Blue bon - net, blue

bon - nie! He's fore - most 'mang the mo - ny Keel lads o' coal - y
earn - ing; Yet right frae wrang dis - cern - ing, Though brave, nae bruis - er
bon - net, He wears a blue bon - net, A dim - ple's in his

Tyne. He'll set or row sae tight - ly, Or in the dance sae
he. Though he no worth a plack is, His ain coat on his
chin; And weel__ may the keel row, The keel row, the

spright - ly, He'll cut and shuf - fle sight - ly, 'Tis true, were he not mine.
back__ is, And nane can say that black is The white o' John - nie's e'e.
keel__ row, And weel__ may the keel row, That my__ lad's__ in.

Chorus:

Weel may the keel row, the keel row, the keel__ row,

Weel may the keel row, That my_____ lad's____ in.

LADY D'ARBANVILLE
Words & Music by Cat Stevens

THE LAST THING ON MY MIND

Words & Music by Tom Paxton

It's a les-son too late for the learn-ing, Made of sand, made of
rea-son a-plen-ty for go-ing, This I know, this I
lie in my bed in the morn-ing With-out you, with-out

sand. In the wink of an eye my soul is turn-ing ___ In your
know, For the weeds have been stead-i-ly grow-ing. ___ Please don't
you. Each song in my breast dies a-born-ing ___ With-out

hand, in your hand.
go, please don't go.
you, with-out you. } Are you go - ing a-way ___ with no

word of fare-well, Will there be not a trace ___ left be-hind? ___ Well I

could have loved ___ you bet-ter, did-n't mean to be un-kind, ___ You know

1-2 that was the last ___ thing on ___ my mind. 2. You've got
3. As I

3 mind, That was the last ___ thing on my mind.

61

LAVENDER BLUE
Traditional

62

MAGGIE MAY
Traditional

Lively

INTRODUCTION: Now ga - ther round, you sai - lor boys, and lis - ten to my plea, And

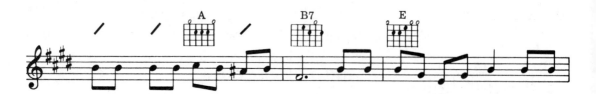

when you've heard my tale, you'll pi - ty me.   For   I   was   a god - damn fool in the

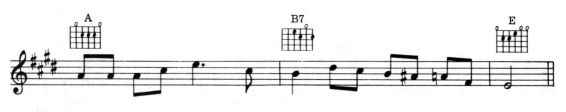

port of Liv - er - pool   The   first   time that   I came home from   sea.

VERSE/CHORUS:

1. We   paid off   at   the home, from the   port of Sie - rra Leone, And

four pounds ten   a   month was my   pay.   With   a pock-et full of tin   I   was

ve - ry soon tak-en in By a girl with the name of Mag - gie May.

CHORUS:

Oh! Maggie, Maggie May, they have taken her away
And she'll never walk down Lime Street any more,
For she robbed so many sailors and captains of the whalers,
That dirty, robbing no-good Maggie May.

2. Oh, well do I remember when I first met Maggie May,
   She was cruising up and down old Canning Place.
   She'd a figure so divine like a frigate of the Line,
   So me being a sailor, I gave chase.

   CHORUS

3. Next morning I awoke, I was flat and stoney broke.
   No jacket, trousers, waistcoat could I find
   When I asked her where they were, she said; "My very dear sir,
   They're down in Kelly's knocker, number nine."

   CHORUS

4. To the pawnshop I did go, but no clothes there did I find,
   And the policeman came and took that girl away.
   The judge, he guilty found her of robbing a homeward-bounder
   And paid her passage back to Botany Bay.

   CHORUS

63

MAMA TOLD ME NOT TO COME
Words & Music by Randy Newman

Moderately, with a beat

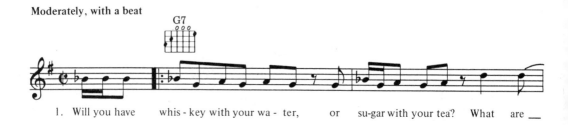

1. Will you have whis-key with your wa-ter, or su-gar with your tea? What are

these cra-zy ques-tions that you're ask-in' of me? This is

the wild-est par-ty that there ev-er could be. Oh, don't

turn on the lights 'cause I don't want to see.

CHORUS

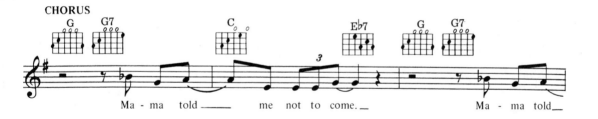

Ma - ma told _____ me not to come. _ Ma - ma told _

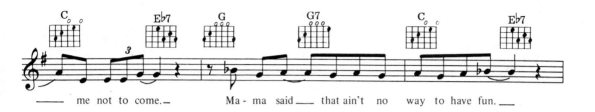

_____ me not to come. _ Ma - ma said _ that ain't no way to have fun. _

Will you have

Verse 2: Open up the window, let some air into this room
I think I'm almost chokin' on the smell of stale perfume
And the cigarette you're smokin's 'bout to scare me half to death
Oh, open up the window, let me catch my breath.   (Chorus)

3. The radio is blastin', someone's knockin' on the door
Our hostess is not lastin', she's passed out on the floor
I've seen so many things that I ain't never seen before
I don't know what it is, but I don't wanna see no more. (Chorus)

64

THE MIDNIGHT SPECIAL
Traditional

Fast, with a steady beat

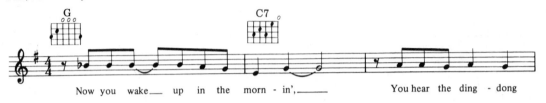

Now you wake___ up in the morn - in',_____ You hear the ding - dong

ring;_____ And you go march - in' to the ta - ble,___

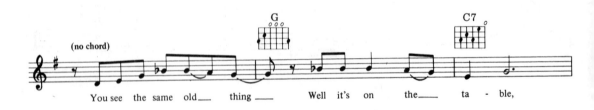

(no chord)

You see the same old___ thing___ Well it's on the___ ta - ble,

A knife, a fork and a pan;_____ But if you say an - y - thing a -

(no chord)

bout it,_____ You're___ in trou - ble with the man!

Chorus:

Oh, let the mid-night spe-cial___ shine her light on

me.___ Oh, let the mid-night spe-cial___

(no chord)

shine her ev-er lov-in' light on me.

2 Well, if you ever go to Houston,
  Man, you'd better walk right.
  And you'd better not stagger,
  And you'd better not fight.
  Because the sherrif will arrest you,
  He's gonna take you down.
  And when the jury finds you guilty,
  You're penitentiary bound.
      Chorus: Oh, let the midnight special. . .

3 Well, yonder comes Miss Rosie
  How in the world did you know?
  Well, I knew by her apron
  And the dress that she wore.
  Well, she brought me a little coffee,
  And she brought me a little tea,
  Well, she brought me nearly ev'rything,
  Except the jailhouse key!
      Chorus: Oh, let the midnight special. . .

65

MR TAMBOURINE MAN

Words & Music by Bob Dylan

Moderato

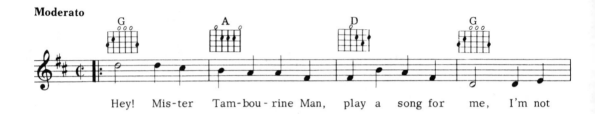

Hey! Mis-ter Tam-bou-rine Man, play a song for me, I'm not

sleep-y and there is no place I'm go-in' to. _____

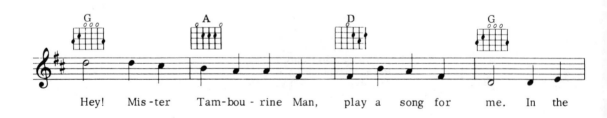

Hey! Mis-ter Tam-bou-rine Man, play a song for me. In the

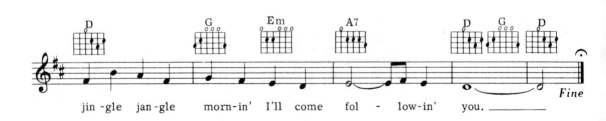

jin-gle jan-gle morn-in' I'll come fol-low-in' you. _____ *Fine*

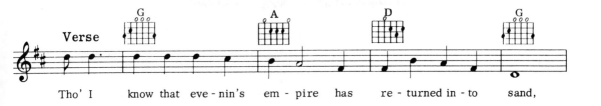

Verse — Tho' I know that eve-nin's em-pire has re-turned in-to sand,

Van-ished from my hand, Left me blind-ly here to stand, but still not

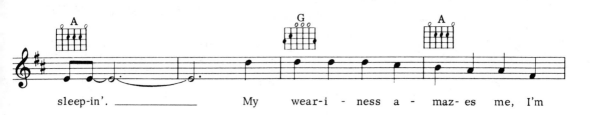

sleep-in'. _____ My wear-i-ness a-maz-es me, I'm

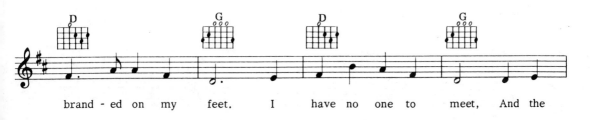

brand-ed on my feet. I have no one to meet, And the

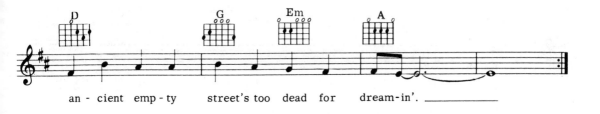

an-cient emp-ty street's too dead for dream-in'. _____

66

THE LIGHTNING TREE
Words & Music by Stephen Francis

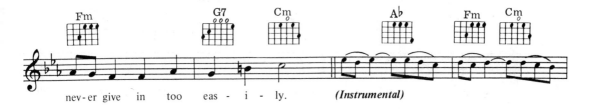

never give in too eas - i - ly. *(Instrumental)*

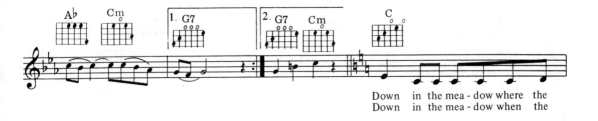

Down in the mea - dow where the
Down in the mea - dow when the

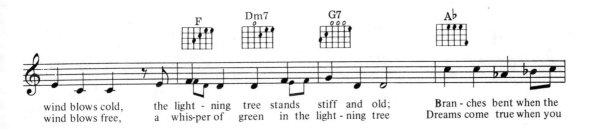

wind blows cold, the light - ning tree stands stiff and old;
wind blows free, a whis-per of green in the light - ning tree

Bran - ches bent when the
Dreams come true when you

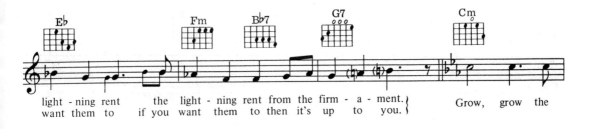

light - ning rent the light - ning rent from the firm - a - ment.
want them to if you want them to then it's up to you.

Grow, grow the

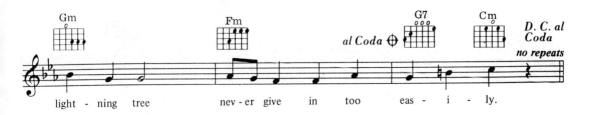

light - ning tree nev - er give in too eas - i - ly.

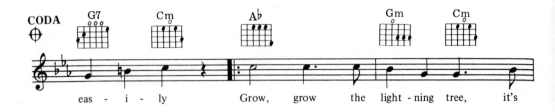

CODA

eas - i - ly   Grow, grow the light - ning tree, it's

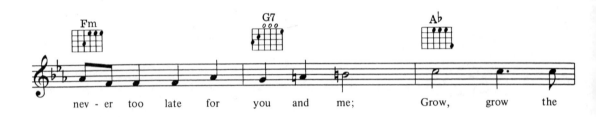

nev - er too late for you and me;   Grow,   grow   the

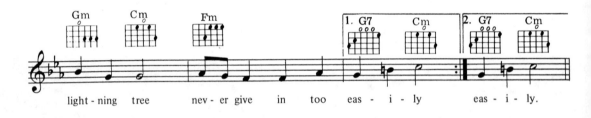

light - ning tree   nev - er give in too eas - i - ly   eas - i - ly.

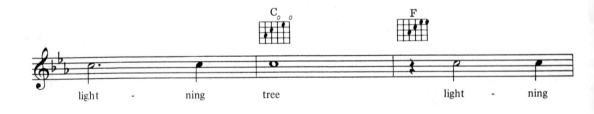

light - ning   tree   light - ning

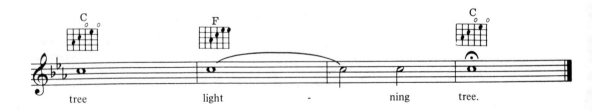

tree   light - ning tree.

67

MOONSHADOW

Words & Music by Cat Stevens

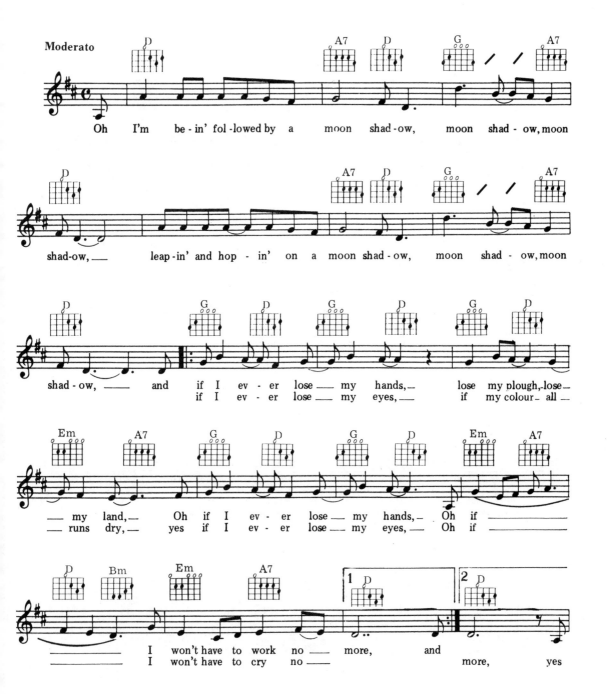

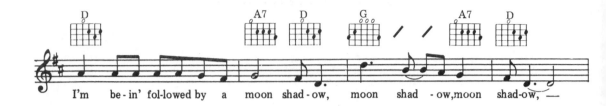

I'm be-in' fol-lowed by a moon shad-ow, moon shad-ow, moon shad-ow, __

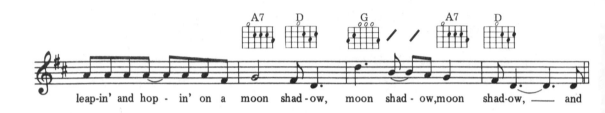

leap-in' and hop-in' on a moon shad-ow, moon shad-ow, moon shad-ow, ___ and

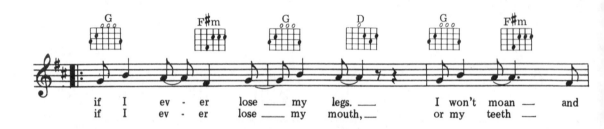

if I ev - er lose __ my legs. __ I won't moan __ and
if I ev - er lose __ my mouth, __ or my teeth __

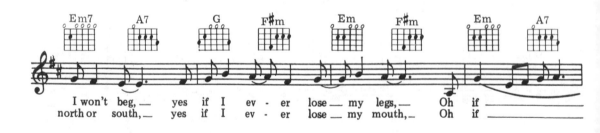

I won't beg, __ yes if I ev - er lose __ my legs, __ Oh if ___
north or south, __ yes if I ev - er lose __ my mouth, __ Oh if ___

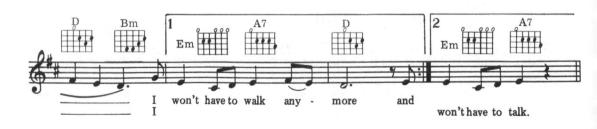

___ I won't have to walk any - more and
___ I won't have to talk.

68

MY FATHER

Words and Music by Judy Collins

Lyrically, nostalgic

(Instrumental 8va)   My

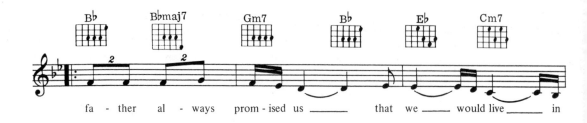

fa - ther al - ways prom - ised us _____ that we _____ would live _____ in

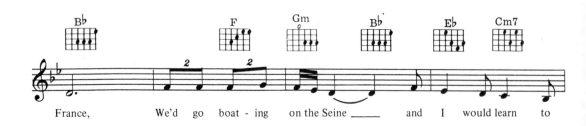

France,   We'd go boat - ing on the Seine _____ and I would learn to

dance.   We lived in O - hi - o then; _____

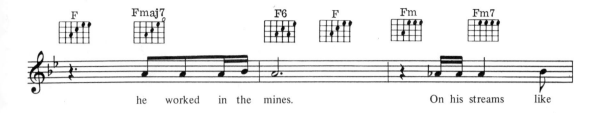

he worked in the mines. On his streams like

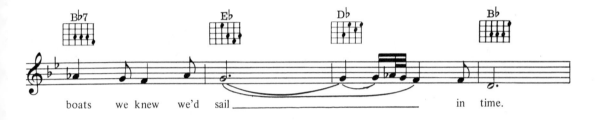

boats we knew we'd sail _____ in time.

(Instrumental)

2. All my sisters soon were gone
   to Denver and Cheyenne,
Marrying their grownup dreams,
   the lilacs and the man.
I stayed behind the youngest still,
   only danced alone,
The colors of my father's dreams
   faded without a sigh.

3. And I live in Paris now,
   my children dance and dream
Hearing the ways of a miner's life
   in words they've never seen.
I sail my memories afar
   like boats across the Seine,
And watch the Paris sun
   set in my father's eyes again.

4. *Repeat 1st Verse*

MORNING HAS BROKEN

Words by Eleanor Farjeon
Music by Cat Stevens

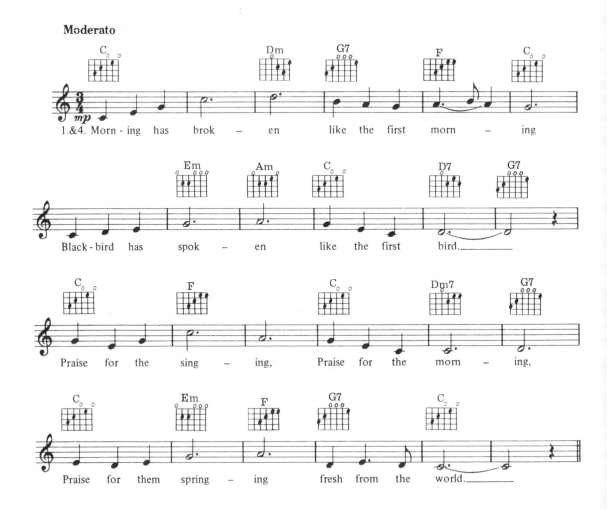

2. Sweet the rains new fall, sunlit from heaven,
   Like the first dew fall, on the first grass.
   Praise for the sweetness of the wet garden,
   Sprung in completeness where His feet pass.

3. Mine is the sunlight, mine is the morning,
   Born of the one light Eden saw play.
   Praise with elation, Praise ev'ry morning,
   God's recreation of the new day.

MY LOVE IS LIKE A RED RED ROSE

Traditional

Slowly, with feeling

My love is like a red, red rose that's
A' the seas gang dry, my dear, and the

new - ly sprung in June, My_ love is like a mel-o - dy that's sweet-ly played in tune. As
rocks meet with the sun, And_ I will love thee still, my dear, while the sands of life shall run. But

fair art thou, my bon - nie lass, so deep in love am I____ And____
fare - thee - well my on - ly love! oh fare - thee - well a while!_ And____

I will love thee still, my dear till a' the seas gang dry; Till
I will come a - gain, my love, tho' 'twere ten thous - and miles. Tho'

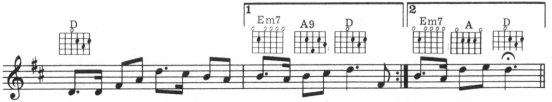

a' the seas gang dry, my dear, till a' the seas gang dry And____
'twere ten thous - and miles, my love, tho' 'twere ten thous - and miles, And____

I will love thee still my dear, Till a' the seas gang dry. (2) Till
I will come a - gain, my love, Tho'   'twere ten thous-and miles.

THE ROVING KIND

New Words & Music Adaptation by Jessie Cavanaugh & Arnold Stanton

Moderato

1. As I set out one eve - ning up - on a night's ca -

reer, I spied a lof - ty fire ship and

toward her I did steer. I hoist - ed up my

sig - nal, a sig - nal that she knew, And

when she saw my bunt - ing up, she sud - den - ly hove to.

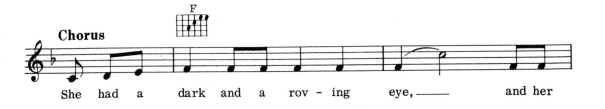

Chorus

She had a dark and a rov-ing eye, —— and her

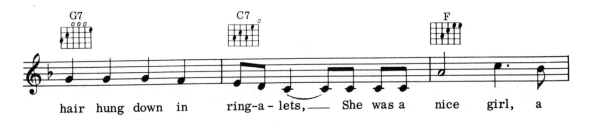

hair hung down in ring-a-lets, —— She was a nice girl, a

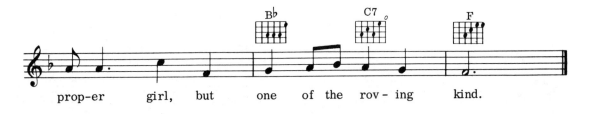

prop-er girl, but one of the rov-ing kind.

2. "Oh sir, please pardon me," she said, "for being out so late,
   And if my parents heard of this then sad would be my fate,
   My father is a minister a fine and righteous man,
   My mother is a chorus girl, I do the best I can."

3. We headed for the village inn, I took her there to dine,
   O little did I ever guess she was the roving kind.
   I hugged her and I kissed her, but much to my surprise
   She really was a fire ship rigged up in a disguise.

4. So hear me well, you sailormen who sail the stormy sea,
   Be careful of those fire ships wherever you may be.
   Beware of them, steer clear of them, they'll cause your ruin, too,
   That's where I lost my rudder and met my Waterloo.

72

PHOTOGRAPHS AND MEMORIES
Words & Music by Jim Croce

Moderately

Pho - to - graphs and mem - o - ries,
Sum - mer skies and lul - la - bies,
Christ-mas cards you
Nights we could-n't

sent to me; _____
say good - bye; _____ And of
All that I have are
all of the things that we

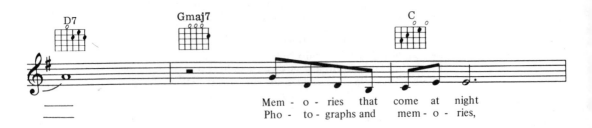

these _____
knew _____
to re - mem - ber you. _____
not a dream sur - vived.

_____ Mem - o - ries that come at night
_____ Pho - to - graphs and mem - o - ries,

Take me to an - oth - er time;__ Back to a hap - pi - er
All the love you gave to me; __ Some - how it just can't be

day, _____ When I called you mine. _____ But
true _____ That's all I've left of you. _____

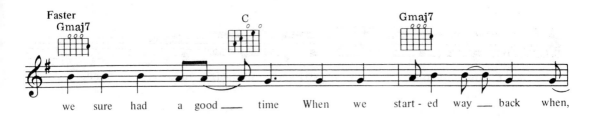

we sure had a good __ time When we start - ed way __ back when,

__ Morn - ing walks __ and bed - room talks, Oh,

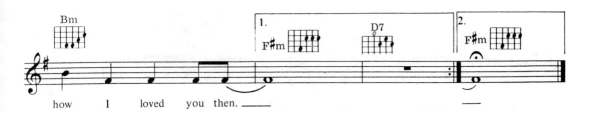

how I loved you then. __

THE PREACHER AND THE BEAR
Traditional

bear sat down up - on the ground and the preach-er climbed on a limb. He

raised his eyes to the God in the skies and these words he said — to Him:

Chorus

"Oh, Lord, did-n't you de - liv - er Dan-iel from the li-on's den? And

so, —— de-liv-er Jo-nah —— from the bel-ly of the whale and then, The

He-brew chil-dren from the fire - y fur-nace so the good books do — de - clare. Now

Lord, if you can't help me — for good-ness sake don't help — that bear."

2. The preacher stayed up in the tree, I think it was all night,
   He said, "Oh, Lord, please help me, or I'll never win this fight!"
   It was just then that the limb gave 'way and the preacher came tumbling
      down,
   Now he had started running before he touched the ground.
   The bear was not to be outdone, right after the preacher he flew,
   And then he up and grabbed him, and squeezed him half in two;
   The preacher, he put up a fight, but the bear held on with a vim,
   He raised his eyes to the God in the skies, and once more he said to Him:

CHORUS

ON TOP OF OLD SMOKEY
Traditional

1. On top of old Smok - y _____ All cov - ered with

snow, _____ I lost my true lov - er _____

_____ By _ court - ing to slow. _____

2. Oh, courting is pleasure and parting is grief,
   But a false hearted lover is worse than a thief.

3. A thief will just rob you of all that you save,
   But a false-hearted lover will lead to the grave.

4. The grave will decay you and turn you to dust,
   Not one in a million a poor girl (boy) can trust.

5. They'll kiss you and squeeze you and tell you more lies
   Than the rain drops from heaven, or stars from the skies.

6. They'll swear that they love you your heart for to please,
   But as soon as your back's turned, they'll love who they please.

7. It's raining and hailing this cold, stormy night,
   Your horses can't travel for the moon gives no light.

8. So put up your horses, and give them some hay,
   And come sit beside me as long as you stay.

9. My horses aren't hungry, they don't want your hay,
   I'm anxious to leave so I'll be on my way.

10. (repeat the first verse).

RAINY DAY MAN
Words & Music by James Taylor

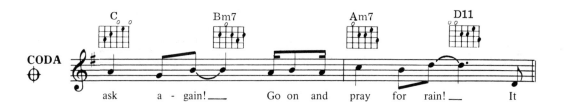

CODA

ask a - gain! ___ Go on and pray for rain! __ It

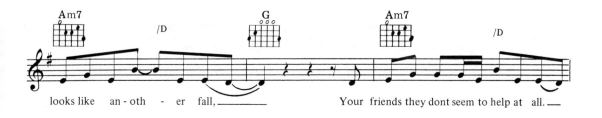

looks like an - oth - er fall, _____ Your friends they dont seem to help at all. __

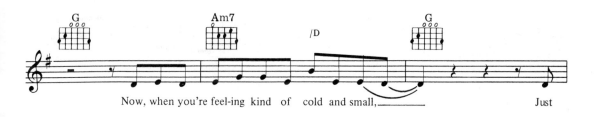

Now, when you're feel-ing kind of cold and small, _____ Just

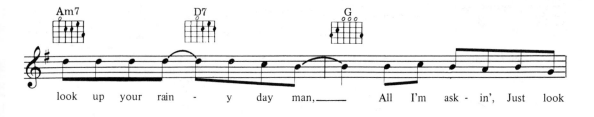

look up your rain - y day man, ____ All I'm ask - in', Just look

to

look up _____ your rain - y day man. _____

76

RIO GRANDE
Traditional

1. O say, were you ev-er in Ri-o Grande? A-

way,_____ Ri-o,_____ It's there that the riv-er runs

down gold-en sand, And we're bound for the Ri-o Grande._____

Chorus
And a-way,_____ Ri-o,_____ A-

way,_____ Ri - o,_____ So fare___ you well, my

bon - nie young girl, And we're bound for the Ri - o Grande._____

2. Oh, New York City is no place for me, away, Rio,
   I'll pack my bags and then I'll go out to sea,
   We're bound for the Rio Grande.

3. The anchor's aweigh and the sails they are set,
   The girls we are leaving we'll never forget, etc.

4. So pack up your sea bag and get under way,
   Perhaps we'll return again another day, etc.

5. A jolly good mate and a jolly good crew,
   A jolly good ship and a good skipper, too, etc.

6. Now you lovely ladies, we would let you know,
   That the time has come, and we're about to go, etc.

7. Sing goodby to Sally, and goodby to Sue,
   And to all you listening, it's goodby, too, etc.

77

SCARBOROUGH FAIR
Traditional

Moderately, with feeling

1. Where are you go - ing? To Scar - bo - rough Fair?
3. Tell her to wash it in yon - der well,
5. Tell her to plough it with one ____ ram's horn,

Pars - ley, sage, ___ rose - ma - ry and thyme, Re - mem - ber me to a
Pars - ley, sage, ___ rose - ma - ry and thyme, Where wa - ter ne'er sprung nor a
Pars - ley, sage, ___ rose - ma - ry and thyme, And sow it all o - ver with

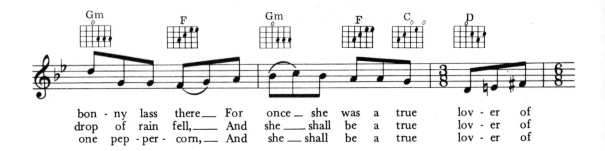

bon - ny lass there ___ For once ___ she was a true lov - er of
drop of rain fell, ___ And she ___ shall be a true lov - er of
one pep - per - corn, ___ And she ___ shall be a true lov - er of

mine. 2. Tell her to make me a cam - bric shirt,
mine. 4. Tell her to plough me an a - cre of land,
mine. 6. Tell her to reap it with a sick - le of leath - er,

Pars - ley, sage___ rose - ma - ry and thyme, With out___ a - ny nee - dle or
Pars - ley, sage,___ rose - ma - ry and thyme, Be - tween___ the sea and the
Pars - ley, sage,___ rose - ma - ry and thyme, And tie it all up with a

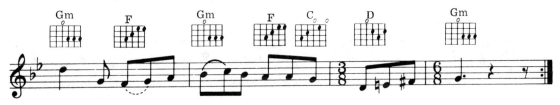

thread work'd in it, And she___ shall be a true lov - er of mine.
salt sea strand,_ And she___ shall be a true lov - er of mine.
tom - tit's feath-er, And she___ shall be a true lov - er of mine.

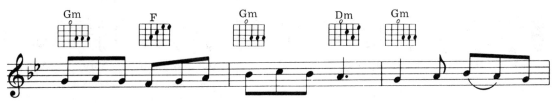

7. Tell her to gath - er it all in a sack, Pars - ley, sage,___ rose -

- ma - ry and thyme, And car - ry it home on a but - ter - fly's back,_ And

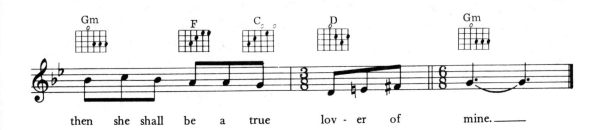

then she shall be a true lov - er of mine._____

78

SHE WORE A YELLOW RIBBON
Traditional

Moderato

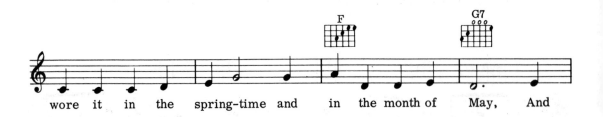

1. Round her neck she wore a yel-low rib-bon, She

wore it in the spring-time and in the month of May, And

if you asked her why she al-ways wore it, She'd

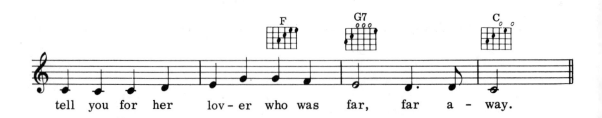

tell you for her lov-er who was far, far a-way.

Chorus

Far a - way, ———— far a - way, ———— She'd

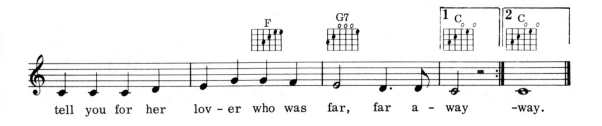

tell you for her lov - er who was far, far a - way -way.

2. Round her neck she wore a golden locket,
   She wore it in the night time and wore it every day,
   And if you asked her why she always wore it,
   She'd tell you for her lover who was far, far away.

3. On her hearth she kept a fire burning,
   She kept it fall and winter, and in the month of May,
   And if you asked her why she always kept it,
   She'd tell you for her lover who was far, far away.

4. Saved her love, and saved her warmest kisses,
   She saved them fall and winter, and in the month of May,
   And if you asked her why she always saved them,
   She'd tell you for her lover who was far, far away.

She Moved Through The Fair

Traditional

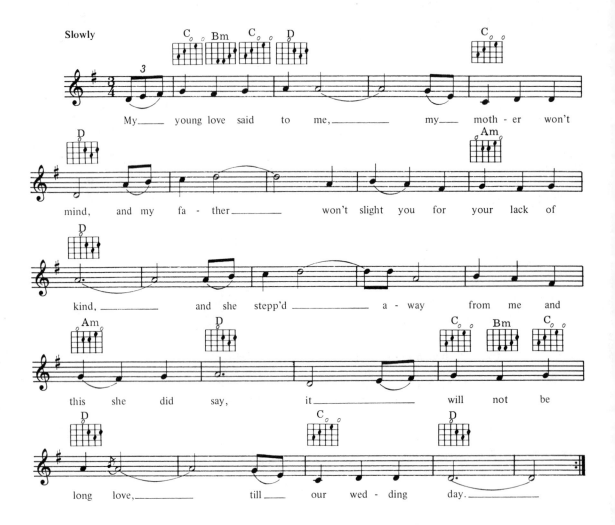

My____ young love said to me,_____ my____ moth - er won't mind, and my fa - ther_____ won't slight you for your lack of kind,_____ and she stepp'd_____ a - way from me and this she did say, it_____ will not be long love,_____ till____ our wed - ding day.____

2. She went away from me, and went through the fair,
    And finally I watched her, move here and move there,
    Then she went homeward with one star awake —
    As the swan in the evening moves over the lake,

3. The people were saying no two were e'er wed,
    But one had a sorrow that never was said,
    She went away from me with her goods and her gear,
    And that was the last that I saw of my dear.

4. Last night she came to me, my dear love came in,
    So softly she came that her feet made no din,
    She laid her hand on me, and this she did say:
    'It will not be long, love, 'till our wedding day.'

SINCE YOU'VE ASKED
Words & Music by Judy Collins

Quietly

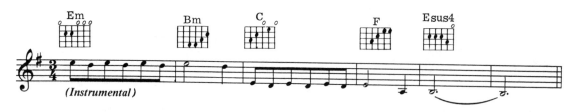

(Instrumental)

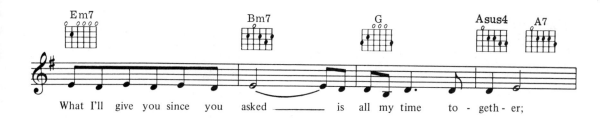

What I'll give you since you asked _____ is all my time to - geth - er;

Take the rug - ged, sun - ny days, _____ the warm and Rock-y weath - er,

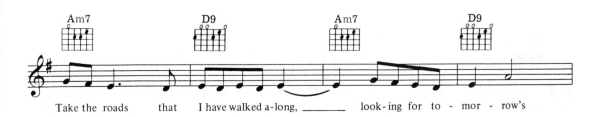

Take the roads that I have walked a-long, _____ look-ing for to - mor - row's

SHENANDOAH
Traditional

Moderato

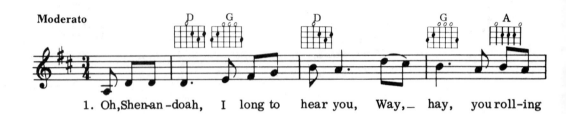

1. Oh, Shen-an-doah, I long to hear you, Way,— hay, you roll-ing

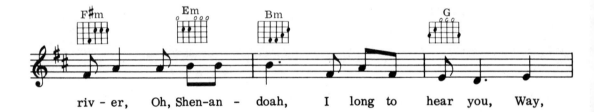

riv - er, Oh, Shen-an - doah, I long to hear you, Way,

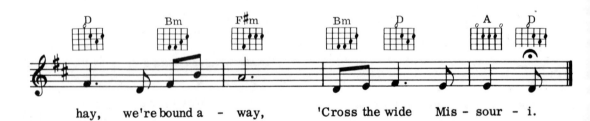

hay, we're bound a - way, 'Cross the wide Mis - sour - i.

2. Oh, Shenandoah, I love your daughter,
Way, hay, you rolling river,
Oh, Shenandoah, I love your daughter,
Way, hay, we're bound away,
'Cross the wide Missouri.

3. Oh, Shenandoah, I love her truly,
Way, hay, you rolling river,
Oh, Shenandoah, I love her truly,
Way, hay, we're bound away,
'Cross the wide Missouri.

4. I long to see your fertile valley,
Way, hay, you rolling river,
I long to see your fertile valley,
Way, hay, we're bound away,
'Cross the wide Missouri.

5. Oh, Shenandoah, I'm bound to leave you,
Way, hay, you rolling river,
Oh, Shenandoah, I'm bound to leave you,
Way, hay, we're bound away,
'Cross the wide Missouri.

SKYE BOAT SONG
Traditional

Slowly, but rhythmically

Chorus: Speed bon-nie boat, like a bird on the wing, On - ward the sail - ors cry!__

Car - ry the lad that is born to be king, O - ver the sea to Skye!__ Skye!__

Verse: Loud the winds howl, Loud the waves roar, thun - der - claps rend the air,_____

Baf - fled our foes stand on the shore, Fol - low they will not dare.__

2. Though the waves leap, soft shall ye sleep,
Ocean's a royal bed;
Rocked in the deep, Flora will keep
Watch by your weary head.

CHORUS

3. Many's the lad fought on that day,
Well the claymore could wield
When the night came, silently lay
Dead on Culloden's field.

CHORUS

4. Burned are our homes, exile and death
Scatter the loyal men;
Yet, e'er the sword cool in the sheath,
Charlie will come again.

CHORUS

STREETS OF LONDON
Words & Music by Ralph McTell

Moderato

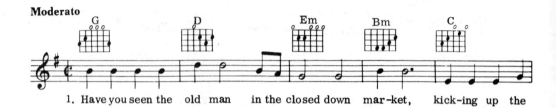

1. Have you seen the old man in the closed down mar-ket, kick-ing up the

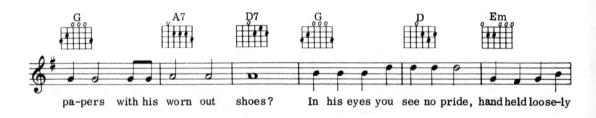

pa-pers with his worn out shoes? In his eyes you see no pride, hand held loose-ly

by his side, _ Yes-ter-day's pa-per tell-ing yes-ter-day's news. _____ So

Chorus

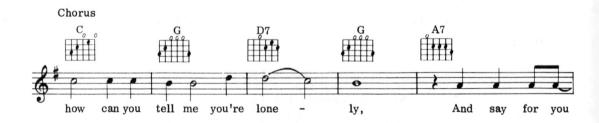

how can you tell me you're lone - ly, And say for you

that the sun don't shine? _____ Let me take_you by the hand,_and

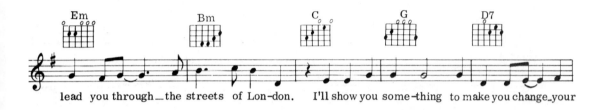

lead you through_the streets of Lon-don. I'll show you some-thing to make you change_your

mind.

2. Have you seen the old girl who walks the streets of London,
   Dirt in her hair and her clothes in rags?
   She's no time for talking, she just keeps right on walking,
   Carrying her home in two carrier bags. (to Chorus)

3. In the all night cafe at a quarter past eleven,
   Same old man sitting there on his own,
   Looking at the world over the rim of his teacup,
   Each tea lasts an hour, and he wanders home alone. (to Chorus)

4. Have you seen the old man outside the seaman's mission,
   Memory fading with the medal ribbons that he wears?
   In our winter city the rain cries a little pity,
   For one more forgotten hero and a world that doesn't care. (to Chorus)

Sundown

Words & Music by Gordon Lightfoot

SWEET BABY JAMES
Words & Music by James Taylor

86

SWEET BETSY FROM PIKE
Traditional

Moderato

1. Did you ev - er hear of sweet Bet - sy from Pike, Who crossed the wide prai - ries with her hus - band Ike, With two yoke of ox - en, a big yel - low dog, A___ tall Shang - hai roost - er, and one spot - ted hog, Sing - ing too ra li oo ra li oo ra li ay?

2. One evening quite early they camped on the Platte,
   Up close to the road on a green grassy flat,
   Poor Betsy, sore footed, lay down for repose,
   And Ike sat and gazed at his Pike County rose,
   Singing too ra li oo ra li oo ra li ay.

3. The alkali desert was burning and bare,
   And Ike cried in fear, "We are lost, I declare!
   My dear old Pike County, I'll come back to you!"
   Vowed Betsy, "You'll go by yourself if you do."
   Singing too ra li oo ra li oo ra li ay.

4. Their wagon broke down with a terrible smash,
   And over the prairie rolled all kinds of trash,
   Poor Ike got discouraged, and Betsy got mad,
   The dog drooped his tail and looked terribly sad.
   Singing too ra li oo ra li oo ra li ay.

5. 'Twas out on the desert that Betsy gave out,
   And down in the sand she lay rolling about,
   Poor Ike, half distracted, looked down in surprise,
   Saying "Betsy, get up, you'll get sand in your eyes!"
   Singing too ra li oo ra li oo ra li ay.

6. Then Betsy got up and gazed out on the plain,
   And said she'd go back to Pike County again,
   But Ike heaved a sigh, and they fondly embraced,
   And they headed on west with his arm 'round her waist.
   Singing too ra li oo ra li oo ra li ay.

7. They swam the wide rivers and crossed the high peaks,
   They camped on the prairie for weeks upon weeks,
   They fought with the Indians with musket and ball,
   And they reached California in spite of it all.
   Singing too ra li oo ra li oo ra li ay.

TAKE ME HOME, COUNTRY ROADS
Words & Music by Bill Danoff, Taffy Nivert & John Denver

SUZANNE

Words & Music by Leonard Cohen

Quietly

1. Su - zanne takes you down ___ to her

place by the riv - er, You can hear the boats go by ___ You can

spend the night be - side her, And you know that she's half cra - zy, And that's

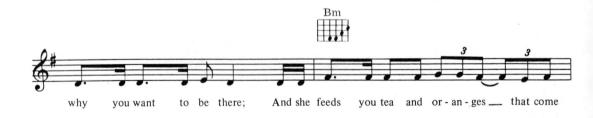

why you want to be there; And she feeds you tea and or - an - ges ___ that come

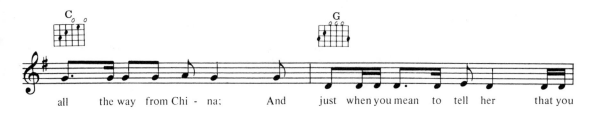

all the way from Chi - na: And just when you mean to tell her that you

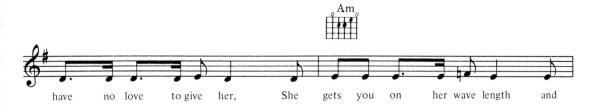

have no love to give her, She gets you on her wave length and

lets the riv-er an - swer that you've al - ways been her lov - er, ____ And you

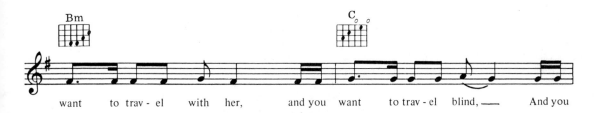

want to trav - el with her, and you want to trav - el blind, ___ And you

know that you can trust her, For you've touched her per - fect bo - dy with your

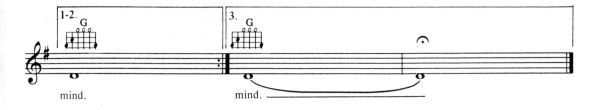

mind.   mind. ____

2. And Jesus was a sailor
   When He walked upon the water,
   And He spent a long time watching
   From a lonely wooden tower,
   And when He knew for certain
   Only drowning men could see Him
   He said, "All men shall be brothers, then,
   Until the sea shall free them,"
   But He Himself was broken
   Long before the sky would open,
   Forsaken, almost human,
   He sank beneath your wisdom
   Like a stone.

   Chorus:
   And you want to travel with Him,
   And you want to travel blind,
   And you think you maybe trust Him,
   For He's touched your perfect body,
   With His mind.

3. Suzanne takes you down
   To her place by the river,
   You can hear the boats go by,
   You can spend the night forever,
   And the sun pours down like honey
   On our lady of the harbour;
   And she shows you where to look
   Amid the garbage and the flowers.
   There are heroes in the seaweed,
   There are children in the morning,
   They are leaning out for love,
   And they will lean that way forever,
   While Suzanne holds the mirror.

   Chorus:
   And you want to travel with her,
   And you want to travel blind,
   And you think maybe you'll trust her,
   For you've touched her perfect body,
   With your mind.

THERE BUT FOR FORTUNE
Words & Music by Phil Ochs

1. Show me ____ the pris - on ____
2. Show me ____ the al - ley ____

Show me ____ the jail, ____   Show me ____ the pris - on - er ____
Show me ____ the train, ____   Show me ____ the ho - bo ____

____ Whose life has gone stale, }   And I'll show you,—
____ Who sleeps out in the rain, }

young man, ____ With so man - y rea - sons ____

why ____ There ____ but for for - tune ____ go

you ____ or I   mm ____

THE TIMES THEY ARE A-CHANGIN'

Words & Music by Bob Dylan

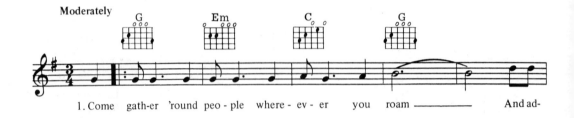

1. Come gath-er 'round peo-ple where-ev-er you roam _____ And ad-

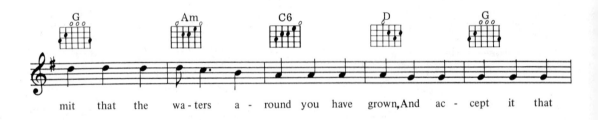

mit that the wa-ters a-round you have grown, And ac-cept it that

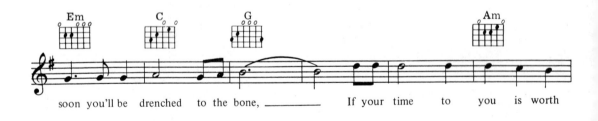

soon you'll be drenched to the bone, _____ If your time to you is worth

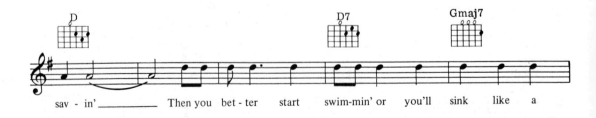

sav-in' _____ Then you bet-ter start swim-min' or you'll sink like a

stone,   For the TIMES   THEY ARE   A – CHANG   -

1-2. G

IN'! _____   2. Come   IN'!
                         3. Come

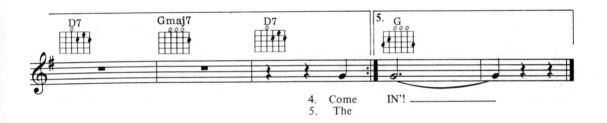

                         4. Come   IN'! _____
                         5. The

2. Come writers and critics
    Who prophecies with your pen
    And keep ycur eyes wide
    The chance won't come again.
    And don't speak too soon
    For the wheel's still in spin
    And there's no tellin' who
    That it's namin'
    For the loser now
    Will be later to win
    For the times they are a-changin'.

3. Come senators, congressmen
    Please heed the call
    Don't stand in the doorway
    Don't block up the hall.
    For he that gets hurt
    Will be he who has stalled
    There's a battle
    Outside and it's ragin'
    It'll soon shake your windows
    And rattle your walls
    For the times they are a-changin'.

4. Come mothers and fathers,
    Throughout the land
    And don't criticize
    What you can't understand.
    Your sons and your daughters
    Are beyond your command
    Your old road is
    Rapidly agin'
    Please get out of the new one
    If you can't lend your hand
    For the times they are a-changin'.

5. The line it is drawn
    The curse it is cast
    The slow one now will
    Later be fast.
    As the present now
    Will later be past
    The order is rapidly fadin'
    And the first one now
    Will later be last
    For the times they are a-changin'.

THE UNIVERSAL SOLDIER
Words & Music by Buffy Sainte-Marie

TUESDAY'S DEAD
Words & Music by Cat Stevens

Fairly Bright Jamaican (in 2)

If I make a mark in time, I can't say the mark is mine. I'm on-ly the un-der line of the word Yes, I'm like him, just like you. I can't tell you what to do. Like ev-ry-bod-y else I'm search-in' thru what I've heard.

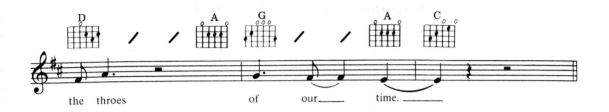

the throes of our___ time. ___

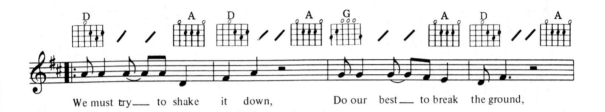

We must try___ to shake it down, Do our best___ to break the ground,

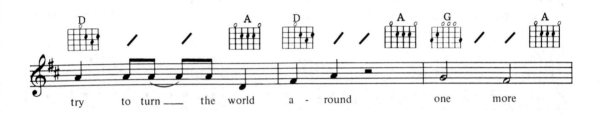

try to turn ___ the world a - round one more

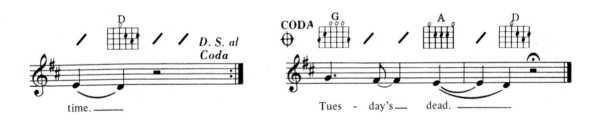

time. ___   Tues - day's ___ dead. ___

Oh preacher won't you paint my dream
won't you show me where you've been,
show me what I haven't seen
to ease my mind
'Cause I will learn to understand
If I have a helping hand
I would'nt make another demand, all my life
Whoa - where do you go when you don't
want no-one to know
Who told to-morrow - Tuesday's dead

What's my sex, what's my name,
all in all it's all the same
everybody plays a different game - that is all
Now man may live, man may die
searching for the question why,
but if he tries to rule the sky - he must fall
Whoa - where do you go when you don't
want no-one to know
Who told you tomorrow - Tuesday's dead
Now every second on the nose
The humdrum of the city grows

TURN, TURN, TURN

Words from the Book of Ecclesiastes
Adaptation and Music by Pete Seeger

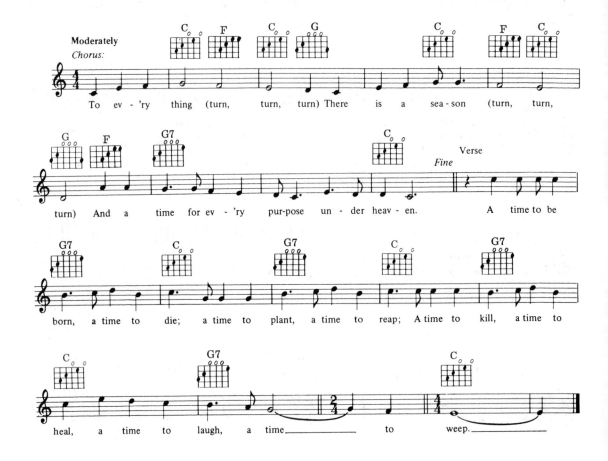

To ev - 'ry thing (turn, turn, turn) There is a sea - son (turn, turn, turn) And a time for ev - 'ry pur - pose un - der heav - en. A time to be born, a time to die; a time to plant, a time to reap; A time to kill, a time to heal, a time to laugh, a time_____ to weep._____

2 A time to build up, a time to break down,
   A time to dance, a time to mourn,
   A time to cast away stones,
   A time to gather stones together.
     Chorus: To everything. . .

3 A time of war, a time of peace,
   A time of love, a time of hate,
   A time you may embrace,
   A time to refrain from embracing.
     Chorus: To everything. . .

4 A time to gain, a time to lose,
   A time to rend, a time to sow,
   A time of love, a time of hate,
   A time of peace I swear, it's not too late.
     Chorus: To everything. . .

94

WHERE HAVE ALL
THE FLOWERS GONE
Words & Music by Pete Seeger

2 Where have all the young girls gone, long time passing?
Where have all the young girls gone, long time ago?
Where have all the young girls gone, gone to young men every one.
When will they ever learn, when will they ever learn?

3 Where have all the young men gone, long time passing?
Where have all the young men gone, long time ago?
Where have all the young men gone, they are all in uniform.
When will they ever learn, when will they ever learn?

4 Where have all the soldiers gone, long time passing?
Where have all the soldiers gone, long time ago?
Where have all the soldiers gone, gone to graveyards every one.
When will they ever learn, when will they ever learn?

5 Where have all the flowers gone, *etc.* . .

WIDDECOMBE FAIR
Traditional

Rhythmically

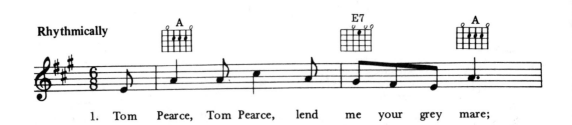

1. Tom Pearce, Tom Pearce, lend me your grey mare;

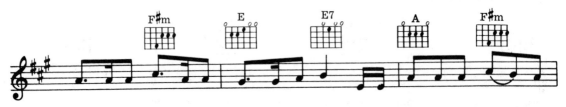

All a - long, down a - long, out a - long lee. For I want for to go___ to

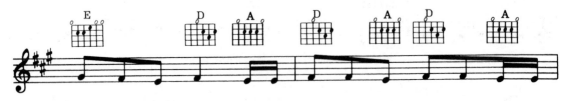

Wid - de - combe Fair, Wi' Bill Brew - er, Jan Stew - er, Pe - ter

Gur - ney, Pe - ter Da - vy, Dan'l Whid-don, Har-ry Hawk, Old Un - cle Tom Cob-leigh and

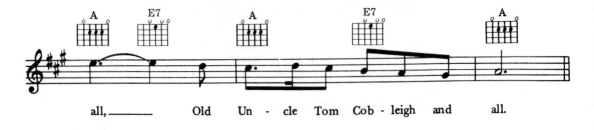

all, ___ Old Un - cle Tom Cob - leigh and all.

2. And when shall I see again my grey mare?
   All along, down along, out along lee.
   By Friday soon or Saturday noon,
   With Bill Brewer, etc.

3. Then Friday came and Saturday noon,
   All along, down along, out along lee.
   But Tom Pearce's old mare hath not trotted home,
   With Bill Brewer, etc.

4. So Tom Pearce he got to the top of the hill,
   All along, down along, out along lee.
   And he see'd his old mare down a-making her will,
   With Bill Brewer, etc.

5. So Tom Pearce's old mare her took sick and died,
   All along, down along, out along lee.
   And Tom he sat down on a stone and he cried,
   With Bill Brewer, etc.

6. But this isn't the end o' this shocking affair,
   All along, down along, out along lee.
   Nor, tho' they be dead, of the horrid career
   Of Bill Brewer, etc.

7. When the wind whistles cold on the moor of a night
   All along, down along, out along lee.
   Tom Pearce's old mare doth appear ghastly white,
   With Bill Brewer, etc.

8. And all the night long be heard skirling and groans
   All along, down along, out along lee.
   From Tom Pearce's old mare in her rattling bones,
   With Bill Brewer, etc.

96

THE WILD COLONIAL BOY
Words & Music by Joseph M. Crofts

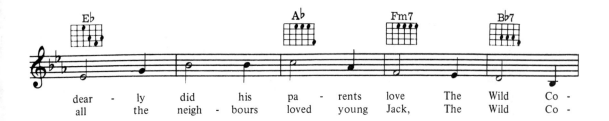

dear - ly did his pa - rents love The Wild Co -
all the neigh - bours loved young Jack, The Wild Co -

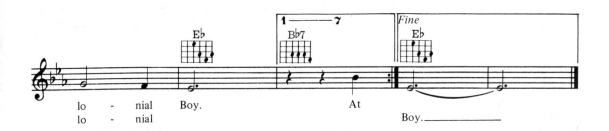

lo - nial Boy.   At
lo - nial   Boy._____

3. At the early age of sixteen years
   He left his native home.
   And to Australia's sunny land
   He was inclined to roam.
   He robbed the rich, and he helped the poor,
   He stabbed James MacEvoy.
   A terror to Australia was
   The Wild Colonial Boy.

4. For two more years this daring youth
   Ran on his wild career.
   With a head that knew no danger
   And a heart that knew no fear.
   He robbed outright the wealthy squires,
   And their Arms he did destroy;
   And woe to all who dared to fight
   The Wild Colonial Boy.

5. He loved the Prairie and the Bush
   Where Rangers rode along:
   With his gun stuck in its holster deep,
   He sang a merry song.
   But if a foe once crossed his track,
   And sought him to destroy,
   He'd get sharp shootin' sure from Jack,
   The Wild Colonial Boy.

6. One morning on the prairie wild,
   Jack Duggan rode along,
   While listening to the mocking bird
   Singing a cheerful song.
   Out jumped three troopers, fierce and grim,
   Kelly, Davis and Fitzroy:
   They all set out to capture him,
   The Wild Colonial Boy.

7. "Surrender now, Jack Duggan, Come!
   You see there's three to one!
   Surrender in the Queen's name, Sir!
   You are a plundering Son!"
   Jack drew two pistols from his side,
   And glared upon Fitzroy:
   "I'll fight, but not surrender!" cried
   The Wild Colonial Boy.

8. He fired a shot at Kelly
   Which brought him to the ground.
   He fired point blank at Davis, too
   Who fell dead at the sound.
   But a bullet pierced his brave young heart
   From the pistol of Fitzroy:
   And that was how they captured him,
   The Wild Colonial Boy.

97

WILD WORLD
Words & Music by Cat Stevens

Moderato

1. Now that I've lost ev-'ry-thing to you ___ you say you wan-na start some-thing new __
2. You know I've seen a lot of what the world can do ___ and it's break-ing my heart in two __

___ and it's break-ing my heart ___ you're leav - ing. Ba-by, I'm griev - in'!
___ be-cause I nev-er want to see you sad, girl. Don't be a bad ___ girl.

But if you want to leave take good care, hope you have a lot of nice things to wear__
But if you want to leave take good care, hope you have a lot of nice friends out there__

___ but then a lot of nice things turn bad out there.__
___ but just re-mem-ber there's a lot of bad and be- ware.__

Oh ba-by, ba - by it's a WILD WORLD. I'ts hard to get by_ just up-on a

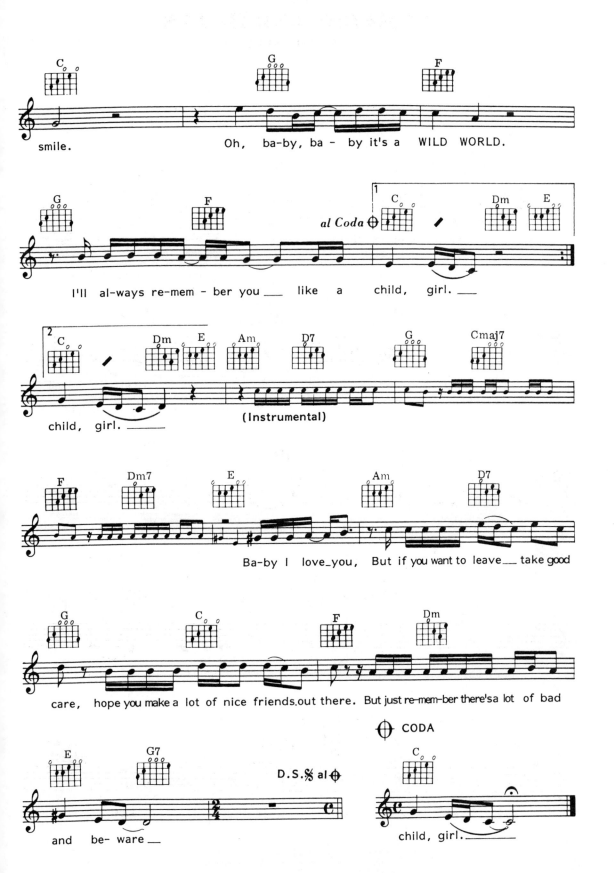

98

YE BANKS AND BRAES
Traditional

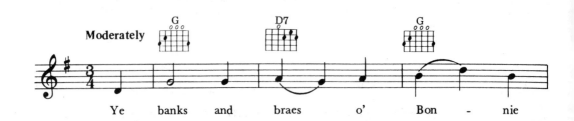

Ye banks and braes o' Bon - nie

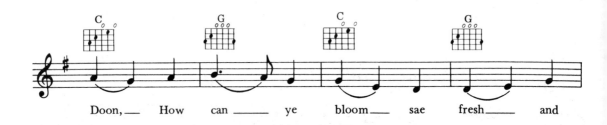

Doon, __ How can __ ye bloom __ sae fresh __ and

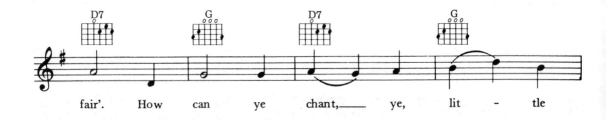

fair'. How can ye chant, __ ye, lit - tle

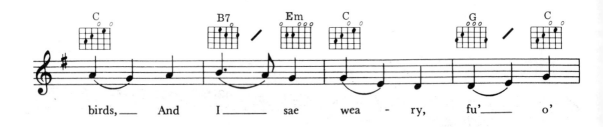

birds, __ And I __ sae wea - ry, fu' __ o'

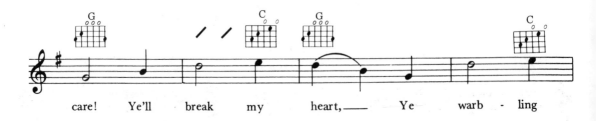

care! Ye'll break my heart, __ Ye warb - ling

bird, That wan - tons thro' the flow'r - ing thorn; Ye

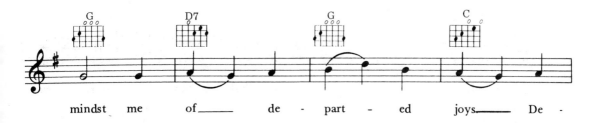

mindst me of_____ de - part - ed joys_____ De -

part - ed, nev - er to_____ re - turn.

2. Oft have I roved by Bonnie Doon,
   To see the rose and woodbine twine;
   And ilka bird sang o' its love,
   And fondly sae did I o' mine.
   Wi' light-some heart, I pu'd a rose,
   Fu' sweet upon its thorny tree;
   And my fause lover stole my rose,
   But ah! he left the thorn wi' me.

99

THE YELLOW ROSE OF TEXAS

Traditional

Moderato

1. There's a yel-low rose in Tex-as that I am going to see, No

oth - er fel - low knows her, no oth - er, on - ly me; She

cried so when I left her, it al-most broke my heart, And

if I ev - er find her, we nev - er more will part.

Chorus

She's the sweet-est rose of Tex - as this fel - low ev - er knew, Her

eyes are bright as dia-monds and spar-kle like the dew; You may

talk a-bout your dear-est maids and sing of Ros - a-lie, But the

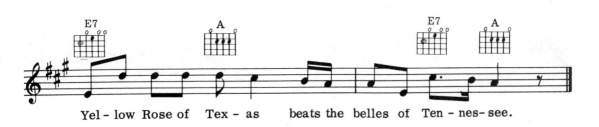

Yel - low Rose of Tex - as beats the belles of Ten - nes-see.

2. Where the Rio Grande is flowing and stars are shining bright,
   We walked along the river one quiet summer night,
   She said, "If you remember, we parted long ago,
   You promised to come back to me and never leave me so."

3. So I'm going back to meet her because I love her so,
   We'll sing the songs together that we sang so long ago,
   I'll play the banjo gaily and we'll sing the songs of yore,
   And the Yellow Rose of Texas shall be mine forevermore.

100

WHAT HAVE THEY DONE TO THE RAIN?

Words & Music by Malvina Reynolds

Moderately

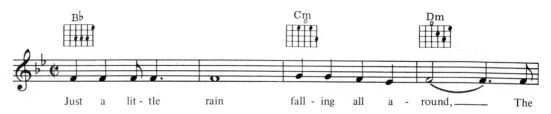

Just a lit-tle rain fall-ing all a-round, _____ The

grass lifts its head _____ to the heav-en-ly sound,

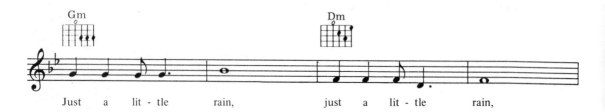

Just a lit-tle rain, just a lit-tle rain,

What have they done _____ to the rain? _____

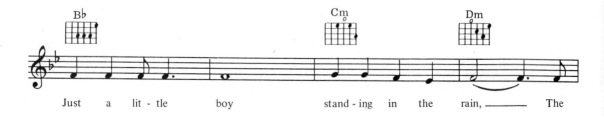

Just a lit-tle boy stand-ing in the rain, _____ The

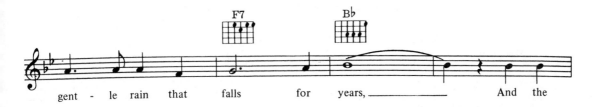

gent - le rain that falls for years, _____ And the

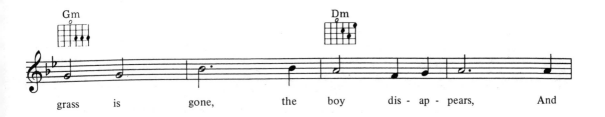

grass is gone, the boy dis - ap - pears, And

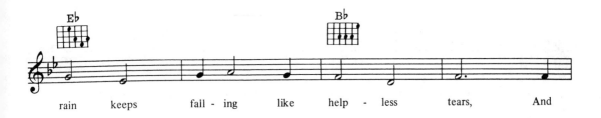

rain keeps fall - ing like help - less tears, And

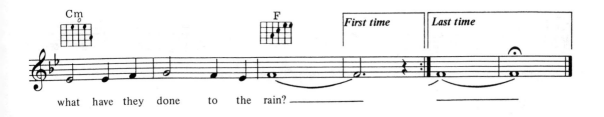

what have they done to the rain? _____

2. Just a little breeze out of the sky,
   The leaves nod their heads as the breeze blows by,
   Just a little breeze with some smoke in its eye,
   What have they done to the rain?

   Just a little boy standing in the rain,
   The gentle rain that falls for years, etc.

101

WABASH CANNONBALL

Words & Music by A.P. Carter

1. From the broad At - lan - tic O - cean to the far Pa - cif - ic shore, On the plains and in the moun - tains you can hear her en - gines roar. She's long, tall, dark, and hand-some, she's loved by one and all, She's a mod - ern lo - co - mo - tive called the Wa-bash Can -non Ball.

2. Hear the moaning of her whistle and the rhythm of her roar
As she races over hill and plain and goes from shore to shore,
As she skims through mighty cities, they hail her one and all,
She's the pride of our entire land, the Wabash Cannon Ball.

3. Now, the eastern states are wonderful, so the western people say,
From New York to old St. Louis and Chicago by the way,
Through the hills of Minnesota where the rippling waters fall,
The finest way to travel's on the Wabash Cannon Ball.

Plus many indispensable collections of special interest:
101 Jazz & Blues Hits ...
101 Showtunes ...
101 Beatles Songs ...
101 Pub Favourites ...
and more.

Busking For Special Occasions 101 Songs:
Piano/Organ/Guitar
AM29596

101 Pub Favourites for Buskers
Piano/Organ/Guitar
AM62761

101 Christmas Hits for Buskers
Piano/Organ/Guitar
AM64569

101 Rock 'n' Roll Hits for Buskers
Piano/Organ/Guitar
AM36484

101 Country Hits for Buskers
Piano/Organ/Guitar
AM33580

101 Australian Songs For Buskers
Piano/Organ/Guitar
AM68073

101 Beatles Songs for Buskers
Piano/Organ/Guitar
N018392

101 Jazz & Blues Hits for Buskers
Piano/Organ/Guitar
AM60245

101 Stage & Screen Hits For Buskers
Piano/Organ/Guitar
AM72612

101 Australian Songs For Buskers, Book 2
Piano/Keyboard/Guitar
AM78684

101 Folk Songs for Buskers
Piano/Organ/Guitar
AM69220

101 Comedy Hits for Buskers
Piano/Organ/Guitar
AM37912

101 Children's Songs For Buskers
Piano/Organ/Guitar
AM74584

101 Showtunes For Buskers
Piano/Organ/Guitar
AM32509

101 Classical Themes For Buskers
Piano/Organ/Guitar
AM65319

101 Pop Hits for Buskers
Piano/Organ/Guitar
AM61763

101 Rock Hits for Buskers
AM65806

101 Rock Hits for Buskers Book 2
AM84716